Henry C. Thacher, Jr.

The Analytical Engine

The
Analytical
Engine

Computers—Past, Present and Future

------- ▶

JEREMY BERNSTEIN

Random House *New York*

Acknowledgments

The author wishes to thank the following authors and publishers for permission to quote from copyright material.

Excerpt on pages ix-x from "The Philosophy of Niels Bohr," by Aage Petersen, in the September 1963 issue of the *Bulletin of the Atomic Scientists*. © Copyright 1963 by Educational Foundation for Nuclear Science, Inc.

Quotations on pages 19, 21-3, 28, 30-4 from *Faster Than Thought,* by B. V. Bowden. Copyright 1953 by Sir Isaac Pitman & Sons, Ltd.

Quotations on pages 25, 26, 62 and 87 from *The Computer and the Brain,* by John von Neumann. © Copyright 1958 by Yale University Press.

Quotation on page 29 from *Automatic Digital Computers,* by M. V. Wilkes. © Copyright 1956 by John Wiley and Sons, Inc.

Quotation on page 59 from "John von Neumann 1903-1957," by Dr. Stanislaw M. Ulam, in the May 1958 issue of the *Bulletin,* Volume 64. © Copyright 1958 by American Mathematical Society.

Quotation on pages 63-4 from an article by P. Armer, in the September 1962 issue of *Datamation*. © Copyright 1962 by Datamation Magazine.

Quotation on page 74 from contribution of J. W. Backus, Proceedings of the Western Joint Computer

To my parents

Preface

------------▶

NIELS BOHR HAD A wonderful way of expressing and criticizing ideas through his humor—"just some little jokes." Recently, I came across one of the stories Bohr loved in an article on his philosophy written by Aage Petersen, who was his assistant in the last years of Bohr's life. As Petersen tells it, "In an isolated village there was a small Jewish community. A famous rabbi once came to the neighboring city to speak and, as the people of the village were eager to learn what the great teacher would say, they sent a young man to listen. When he returned he said, 'The rabbi spoke three times. The first talk was brilliant; clear and simple. I understood every word. The second was even better; deep and subtle. I didn't understand much but the rabbi understood all of it. The third was by far the finest; a great and unforgettable experience. I understood nothing and the rabbi himself didn't understand much either.' "

About the subject of computers, I feel somewhat the way the young man felt about the rabbi. There is a part that I have come to understand on my own (the interested reader will find a bibliography, listing those references that were especially useful to me in this process); there is a part that computer experts have explained to me; and, finally, there is a part that involves things on the frontier of research and not yet completely understood. I have tried to warn the reader when things become speculative—and often these were for me among the most fascinating things to learn and write about—by sprinkling the appropriate sections liberally with "probably's" and "perhaps's."

This book and the articles in *The New Yorker* that it is based on were written with the help of many people. In the first place, most of the people still active in the field who are mentioned in the book, have read parts of the manuscript and I am immensely grateful to them for the time they took in explaining their work and for seeing to it that my version of it was as free of error as possible. In addition to this large group of computer experts, I would like to thank Thomas J. Deegan of I.B.M., who became fascinated by the problem of trying to do a serious article on computers for a wide audience of laymen and who helped me, for nearly a year, to gather a wide range of material. I am also grateful to Robert Gerdy of *The New Yorker* editorial staff for his constant and patient guidance, criticism, and help in what appeared to me at the start to be an almost impossible job in shaping and clarifying the very difficult material in the articles. Finally, I am grateful to William Shawn, the editor of *The New Yorker*, for encouraging me to try to write about such a complex scientific subject for a magazine whose readership is composed of people who are predominantly nonscientists.

The Analytical Engine

THE electronic computer, young as it is, has come
to play a role in modern life something like that
played in other times by the oracles of Greece and
Rome. There is a widespread belief that if one puts
a question to, say, the UNIVAC, it will perform a
swarm of bizarre manipulations—comparable to
the generating of the vapors in the chasm at Del-
phi—and come up, in oracular fashion, with the
answer. It is more realistic, if less awe-inspiring, to
look upon the electronic computer as an over-
grown arithmetic machine. It can add, subtract,

multiply, and divide, and it can perform long sequences of additions, subtractions, multiplications, and divisions, in highly complicated arrangements; it can also modify the course of a calculation as it goes along—that is, choose which of several steps to take next in accordance with the way some previous step came out. Fundamentally, though, all this comes down to arithmetic, and, arithmetically speaking, the distinction between a schoolboy doing a multiplication a minute and a computer doing a hundred thousand multiplications a second is only one of degree. In practice, of course, there is a great difference, for one can turn over to a machine problems of much greater complexity than one would ever think of turning over to a team of expert human computers, let alone a schoolboy. In attempting to forecast the results of an election, for example, one may feed into the computer a vast array of data about prior elections, which the machine can compare almost instantly with corresponding data about the election at hand. This is a purely numerical process, and, given enough time, human computers could make exactly the same comparisons and obtain exactly the same forecasts. Obviously, any such forecasts are only as reliable as the statistical data that go into them. The computer does not invent its own data, and it makes about as much sense to ridicule a computer for coming up with a wrong forecast on the basis of poor data as it does to attribute prescience to the machine for making the right forecast on the basis of good data. The machine in either case is merely an instrument, deserving neither praise nor blame.

My own experience with computers has been that of a theoretical physicist. Frequently, I have run into numerical problems that would have taken weeks of dreary "hand" computation, if, indeed, I could have persisted through to the end at all. Electronic computers do such jobs in a matter of minutes, and after submitting a few problems to the machines I came to regard them with enormous respect. However, it was not until recently that I learned enough about them to, so to speak, negotiate with them myself. There had been a kind of language barrier between us—a barrier that could be surmounted only by an expert intermediary. For one cannot simply present a problem to a machine in English, and expect it to come up with the answer; the computer has a language of its own—machine language—and whatever one wants to tell it must be translated into that language. Early in my experiences with computers, I saw some of these translations—"programs," as they are called—and because they seemed to be an unintelligible array of letters and numbers, arranged in patterns quite unrelated to those used in ordinary English, or in arithmetic or algebra, I came to think of programming as a black art, best left to the professionals. For several years, I prepared my problems, and the instructions for solving them, in language that I knew, and handed the lot over to a programmer, who went on from there. Together, programmers and computers relieved me of a great deal of drudgery, but they also gave me a feeling I didn't like—a feeling of remoteness from my problems.

However, some of my colleagues began telling me that there had been a great revolution in programming—that the job had been made much easier by the invention of several new languages, which stuck remarkably close to the words and symbols of conventional mathematical language, and which the machines more or less translated for themselves. In fact, I was assured that even if one had only a vague idea of how a modern computer worked, one could learn to communicate with it—to some degree, at least—without an interpreter. I was also told that the appropriate language for the sort of scientific computation I customarily ran up against was called FORTRAN (for "Formula Translation"), and that a good many universities occasionally offered short, intensive courses in it, rather like cram courses in Italian or French. New York University, where I teach, has a computing center, which is part of the Courant Institute of Mathematical Sciences. It offers short FORTRAN courses three times a year, and I decided to enroll in one of them. As it turned out, I found that learning something about FORTRAN was an excellent introduction to the subject of computers in general.

Before going to the first lecture, I had assumed that all my fellow FORTRAN students would be professional scientists or engineers, but, in a quick survey, our instructor, an operations associate at the Courant Institute named Howard L. Walowitz, discovered that the class included a librarian and also several women from the university's Department of Nurse Education, who were writing theses involving detailed analyses of medical statistics. Although a few of the students had taken FORTRAN courses elsewhere and were just brushing up, most of us had no knowledge whatever of the language. However, FORTRAN programming is simple enough to learn so that within a couple of days most of us had learned enough about its elements to set up a simple problem and get an answer back from the machine.

The first step in programming is to write down something on something, and Mr. Walowitz started out by showing us the kind of sheet we would write on—a blank FORTRAN coding form. This is a piece of pale-green paper, the size of type-writer paper and ruled off into about fifteen hundred rectangles, each of which can be filled in with a digit, a letter, or a punctuation mark. We were then given a coding form with an easy "model" problem, one that obviously didn't require a multimillion-dollar computer—a simple income-tax computation, in which the tax was to be computed according to the formula:

$$\text{TAX} = 22\% \ (\text{GROSS INCOME} - \$600.00 \times \text{NUMBER OF EXEMPTIONS})$$

At first glance, a FORTRAN program appears somewhat forbidding, but once one understands the role that the different phrases play, one begins to appreciate how precise and even elegant they are. Slightly abbreviated, our model FORTRAN program for doing the tax went like this:

```
1 READ INPUT TAPE 5,
   GROSS, EXMP
TAX = 0.22 * (GROSS — EXMP * 600.0)
   IF (TAX) 2,3,3
   2 TAX = 0.0
3 WRITE OUTPUT TAPE 6,
   GROSS, EXMP, TAX
   GO TO 1
```

It is easy to get the impression from seeing a command like the first one that the machine will respond to any English command—READ PROUST, say. Actually, FORTRAN consists of only a limited number of phrases, which can be put together to convey the sequence of steps needed in solving a great variety of mathematical problems. Most large computers "store" data on reels of magnetic tape, and in this instance the "READ" command informs the machine that it will find the appropriate data—a set of figures for gross income and exemptions—on magnetic tape 5.

Second comes the formula, written very much the way one would normally write it, the main exception being that a few of the symbols are changed to avoid ambiguity. Thus:

$$TAX = 0.22 * (GROSS — EXMP * 600.0)$$

What appears next is one of the most powerful FORTRAN statements—one that illustrates the "decision-making" ability of a modern computer:

IF (TAX) 2,3,3

This statement tells the machine how to proceed after computing the tax, depending on whether the answer is a negative number, zero, or a positive number. If the answer is negative, the machine is to go to Instruction 2, or:

TAX = 0.0

There is no such thing as a negative tax, and Instruction 2 says that if EXMP * 600 should exceed GROSS, the machine is to write out the tax as zero. In this case, practically speaking, one negative answer would mean the same as another—no tax— so the programmer has no interest in just what the negative number is.

If the tax comes out either zero or positive, the machine goes to Instruction 3, which tells it to write out the actual result of the tax computation on another tape. This tape will be used to run a high-speed automatic printer, which will print out the whole computation on paper.

"GO TO 1" instructs the machine to go back to the beginning of the program—that is, to start over again with the next set of figures on Tape 5.

This sequence of instructions enables the machine to compute the tax once the programmer has supplied sets of numerical values for the variables GROSS and EXMP. These values were written under the heading "DATA," just below the instruction sequence. In due course they were transcribed onto Magnetic Tape 5. The program and the data are separate entities, and once the programmer has set up a program, he can use it any time he provides the data.

After the first lecture, we were taken on a brief tour of the N.Y.U. computing center. The center uses two computers in tandem, a relatively small I.B.M. 1401 computer being employed to process data for the much larger I.B.M. 7090. In this setup, getting data into the 7090 is a three-step affair. First, the program on the green sheets is transferred to punch cards, through which a pattern of holes is punched representing the FORTRAN symbols. (This is a mechanical job, much like typing, and it is frequently done by key-punch operators, though one can easily learn to do it oneself.) Second, the cards are fed in a deck into the 1401, which "reads" them—that is, senses the patterns of holes electronically. And, third, the 1401 puts the information on the cards on magnetic tape, which is read directly by the 7090. On most jobs, the 1401 also controls the operation of the automatic printer, which we could see pouring out results obtained from the 7090, at the rate of some six hundred lines a minute. While the machines are in operation, their interior workings are hidden in neat gray metal cases. The reels of magnetic tape, however, are housed in cabinets with glass windows—one reel to a cabinet. It is fascinating to watch the machine work back and forth among the reels in the course of a calculation. A light goes on over one of the cabinets, and the reel inside whirls for a fraction of a second. Then another light goes on, and another reel whirls, and so it goes.

At the next lecture, we received our first homework assignment, and from it I learned that although FORTRAN looks simple, it is full of nuances. Our problem had to do with mortgage amortization, and, like the tax computation, it came down to evaluating a formula—that is, finding the numerical values corresponding to the abstract variables—but this formula was somewhat more complex than the tax formula. We were advised to prepare a "flow chart" before we actually began to write out the program. A flow chart is a diagram illustrating the logical "flow" of steps that must be taken to solve a problem. In preparing it one has to think out, in proper order, the various mathematical and logical operations that one would perform in solving the problem on one's own. On one's own, of course, one often takes operations for granted and performs them almost without thinking. A machine cannot be expected to take anything for granted, and though the process of diagramming the steps is somewhat tedious, one learns after making a few attempts at writing a program without preparing a flow chart, that it is an invaluable way to keep the outline of the program straight. However, the program itself must be made up out of the set phrases and grammatical constructions that constitute the FORTRAN language. So, having decided on the appropriate sequence of operations, and having outlined these on the flow chart, one must find the FORTRAN expressions that will convey one's commands to the machine. Finding just the right expressions to do the job is a little like putting together a jigsaw puzzle, and once one gets the hang of it, it can be a good deal of fun. But FORTRAN has a very finnicky grammar; if one leaves out a comma where the rules say there must be a comma, the machine will simply not accept the program. It was only after three or four unsuccessful attempts that I was able to write out a program with all of the grammatical details correct, and when I got back the printed results of my first computation—the "printout"—I had a feeling of satisfaction of having communicated with the machine that reminded me of the way I felt when after a week of French lessons in Paris I discovered that I was able to engage in useful, if limited, conversations with my concierge.

In doing our second homework problem, which was a lot harder than the first, I learned what happens when a faulty FORTRAN program gets put onto the machine. I had prepared what seemed to me an absolutely foolproof green sheet and had given it to the key-punch operators. After a while, I got my printout, which began with the date and with the title "709/7090 FORTRAN DIAGNOSTIC PROGRAM RESULTS." Next came one of the formulas I had written out, followed by the terse com-

ment "TOO MANY LEFT PARENTHESES." (FORTRAN
grammar, like any other, demands that left and
right parentheses balance out.) I looked at the
formula and saw that the key-punch operator had
taken a slash symbol, which indicates division, for
a left parenthesis. To the machine, the formula
appeared as:

$$\text{STDV} = (\text{SUM} \ (\text{GN}) \ ** \ .5$$

It should have been:

$$\text{STDV} = (\text{SUM} \ / \ \text{GN}) \ ** \ .5$$

When I asked what had happened, I was told
something about the steps the machine takes after
it receives a FORTRAN program. It first scans the
program for any simple grammatical error, like
leaving out a comma. If everything seems in order,
it normally proceeds to translate the FORTRAN into
machine language—a process known as compiling
—and then to carry out the commands, just as a
person given an instruction in a foreign language
would translate it before acting on it. If the machine does pick up some errors in the first scan, it
does not go on with the translation but prints out a
sheet with diagnostic messages that call attention
to the mistakes. Near the bottom of my printout, I
found a set of messages that almost seemed to
grumble:

ILLEGAL USE OF PUNCTUATION . . . SOURCE
PROGRAM ERROR . . . NO COMPILATION . . .
EXECUTION DELETED.

When I pointed these out to Mr. Walowitz, he said he often wished that the machine would simply correct the mistake, go on with its business, and leave one alone. At the end of the sheet, there was a notation that it had taken the machine less than thirty-six seconds to locate the mistake. The speed at which a modern computer works is extremely impressive. Most of the homework problems that we did—they were relatively simple machine computations, to be sure—took less than a minute of machine time. During this time, the machine made the translation from the FORTRAN program into machine language; executed the machine-language program, using whatever data one had supplied; and put the result of the computation onto magnetic tape.

Correcting the program, in my case of "illegal use of punctuation," amounted simply to having the key-punch operator prepare a new card—something that was extremely easy to do, since only one symbol had to be changed. The operator set the key punch to reproduce the original card up to the errant parenthesis, then keyed in the slash symbol by hand, and finally set the key punch to reproduce the rest of the original card.

Most of the errors that the FORTRAN diagnostic program picks up have to do with punctuation. Of course, it is quite possible (even customary) to make other kinds of mistakes—in logic, for example—and the machine will usually not pick these up, though it may catch mistakes that fall somewhere between punctuation and logic. For example, I once wrote a program in which I labelled a statement 9070 and later referred to it as 9060. The machine reacted by printing out:

THE FOLLOWING FORMAT STATEMENTS, THOUGH REFERRED TO, HAVE BEEN OMITTED FROM THE SOURCE PROGRAM . . . 9060

When I asked why the machine didn't diagnose a wider variety of errors, I was told that it would just be a waste of the machine's time. It is much more economical to have the machine spot errors in punctuation and to use the human programmer to spot the more subtle ones.

During the next two weeks, our homework became more and more difficult. One of our most interesting tasks was to program the machine to arrange several hundred numbers in descending order—a problem that involved several uses of the FORTRAN IF statement, which we had been introduced to our first day in class. This time, we used IF statements to instruct the machine to arrange and rearrange the numbers after subtracting them from one another and seeing whether the result was positive, negative, or zero. The exercise also gave us a detailed introduction to FORTRAN DO statements, sometimes known as DO loops. Often in the course of a computation one wishes to repeat a process several times in sequence. A simple, if not very striking, example would be multiplying all of the numbers from 1 to 10, one after the other, by the number 3. One could, of course, write a FORTRAN program involving ten separate multiplication instructions, but this would be a nuisance—and more than a nuisance—if, instead of ten multiplications, one wanted, say, ten thousand. The whole set of instructions can be compressed into two simple commands:

$$\text{DO } 5, \text{I} = 1, 10$$
$$5 \text{ M (I)} = 3 * \text{I}$$

The DO statement here tells the machine to do Instruction 5 for the ten values, and Instruction 5 tells it to multiply the integer I, whatever it happens to be, by 3.

Our class also learned how to make use of "subroutines." In arithmetic work, certain special operations—like taking a square root or a logarithm—are likely to be used many times, and although it would be quite possible to write out in FORTRAN the detailed steps for, say, taking a square root, it is much more economical to write out, once and for all, a square-root program, store it on magnetic tape, and bring it into a calculation whenever it is needed. Computing the square root of quantity F can be called for simply by writing:

$$\text{SQRT (F)}$$

There are about thirty such routines in the normal FORTRAN repertoire, and many other specialized programs and routines are available, thanks to a library in White Plains that is administered by I.B.M. These programs are given out, at no cost, to any computer user, and, in return, the user may supply the library with new programs he has worked out. The library currently contains several thousand programs and is constantly expanding.

Although I hardly qualified as an expert programmer at the end of the two-week course, I did have some understanding of what sort of problems FORTRAN can help one solve, and while none of our homework assignments sprang directly from physics, they involved similar types of calculations, and I felt some confidence in my ability to set up my own problems for the computer. All the time I was taking the course, however, I had an uneasy feeling; what the machine could do became impressively clear to me, but I kept wondering how it did it. When I finished the course, I decided to find out something about the machines, their history, and what we can expect of them in the future.

ii

--------►

NOWADAYS, the ability to perform arithmetical computations is shared by most educated people. In doing computations, memory certainly plays an important role. If one did not know the multiplication table by heart, the simplest arithmetic would become a nightmare, and we take it for granted that just about everybody does know it. This widespread knowledge, however, is quite a recent phenomenon. In a brilliant essay entitled "A Brief History of Computation," written in 1953 and published in a book called *Faster Than Thought*, Dr.

B. V. Bowden, of Ferranti, Ltd., a British computer-manufacturing firm, notes:

> A few hundred years ago the art of computation was neither commonly understood nor widely practised. In 1662, Pepys, who was then in charge of the contracts branch of the Admiralty, found it necessary to put himself to school, and to rise by candlelight at four o'clock in the morning in order to learn his multiplication tables. He had been to Cambridge, and was, by the standards of his time, a well-educated man, [and] in later life he became President of the Royal Society and a friend of Newton, but when he was Clerk of the Acts he found himself quite unable to understand the simple computations which had to be done when buying timber for the King. In those days school boys seldom went beyond "two times two."

Apparently, his efforts were not in vain, for, as Dr. Bowden notes, in December, 1663, Pepys wrote in his diary: "My wife rose anon, and she and I all the afternoon at arithmetique, and she able to do additions, subtractions and multiplications very well, and so I purpose not to trouble her yet with divisions, but show her the use of Globes."

The ability to calculate rapidly varies a great deal, and has nothing at all to do with the ability to grasp the abstractions of higher mathematics; mathematicians, by and large, are not outstanding computers, nor is computational skill vital for creative work in mathematics. In the summer of 1961, I had an opportunity to work with Mr. William Klein, a programmer and numerical analyst for CERN (Centre Européen pour la Recherche Nucléaire), in Geneva, who must be one of the fastest human computers who has ever lived. I was spending the summer doing physics at CERN and had been working with a friend on a problem. After a week or so, we produced an algebraic formula that seemed admirable to us in many respects, and we wanted to evaluate it. CERN has a large Ferranti Mercury computer, and since at the time neither of us knew anything about programming, we asked for help. Enter Mr. Klein. Mr. Klein is a short, kindly, energetic-looking man in his forties. He is of Dutch origin. He looked at our formula for a few seconds, muttering to himself in Dutch, and then gave us numerical estimates for several of the more complex parts of it. Doing this, he said, helped set up the program for the computer in the most efficient way. I had heard about Mr. Klein's almost incredible ability, and I asked him whether he had considered evaluating our whole expression in his head. He told me that it would involve much too much work and that he was quite glad to turn the job over to the machine. Watching Mr. Klein at work made a deep impression on me, and I was delighted to find something about him in another of Dr. Bowden's essays, this one called "Thought and Machine Processes." Dr. Bowden writes:

[Mr. Klein] knows by heart the multiplication tables up to 100 × 100, all squares up to 1000 × 1000, and an enormous number of odd facts, such as 3937 × 127 = 499999, which are very useful to him, and seem to arise instantly in his mind when they are needed. In addition, Mr. Klein [who knows the logarithms of numbers up to 150 to fourteen decimal places] can work out sums like compound interest by "looking up" the logs in his head, after factorizing the numbers he is using, if need be. He has also learnt enough about the calendar to be able to give the day of the week corresponding to any specified date in history.

Dr. Bowden goes on:

Mr. Klein multiplies numbers of up to six digits faster in his head than an ordinary man can do by using a desk calculating machine. For example, he wrote down the products of six pairs of three-digit numbers in nine seconds; an experienced calculating machine operator took a minute to do the same calculations.

Mr. Klein multiplied

1 388 978 361 × 5 645 418 496

= 7 841 364 129 733 165 056

completely in his head, a calculation which involved twenty-five multiplications each of two two-digit numbers and twenty-four addi-

tions of four-digit numbers—forty-nine operations in all—in sixty-four seconds. . . . A
dozen of us tried it [and] the times we took
varied between six and sixteen minutes, and
all our answers were wrong excepting one.

I asked Mr. Klein about this feat, and he told me
that now that he had come to rely on computers,
he was slightly out of practice, and Dr. Bowden's
multiplication would take him a full two minutes.
At any rate, phenomenal ability in computation
apparently runs in the Klein family, for Dr. Bowden adds:

Mr. William Klein's brother Leo, who died
at the hands of the Gestapo during the war,
was almost as good a computer as William
and a better mathematician. Dr. Stokvis of
Amsterdam made a psychological study of the
brothers; he found that although their per-
formances were very similar their methods of
operation were quite different. For example,
Mr. William Klein remembers numbers "audi-
bly"; he mutters to himself as he computes, he
can be interrupted by loud noises, and if he
ever does make a mistake it is by confusing
two numbers which sound alike. Leo, on the
other hand, remembered things "visually";
and if he made a mistake it was by confusing
digits which look alike. Both brothers were
fascinated by numbers from their earliest
childhood. . . . William read medicine, took

a medical degree and had "walked the hospitals" before he decided to earn his living as a computer.

Mr. Klein told me that, after the war, he spent a few years doing mental arithmetic on the stage in Europe under the pseudonym "Pascal," after the mathematician. Mr. Klein's very reasonable unwillingness to spend more time than necessary these days on the mental drudgery of computation is, of course, akin to the feeling that led to the invention of mechanical calculating devices. As Leibnitz wrote in 1671, "It is unworthy of excellent men to lose hours like slaves in the labor of calculation which could safely be relegated to anyone else if machines were used."

Calculating machines have been of two fundamental types—analogue and digital. The analogue machines represent numbers by some analogous quantity, such as length or size. A child might learn to add by assembling blocks of various sizes; a block of a given size would be the analogue of 1, a block twice the size the analogue of 2, and so on. The most widely used analogue calculator is the ordinary slide rule, which was invented in 1622 by the English mathematician William Oughtred, and which is suitable for many rough-and-ready calculations. On the slide rule, numbers are represented by lengths; so much slide rule corresponds essentially to so much number. What limits accuracy in using the slide rule is the limited ability of the eye; it is quite easy to get accuracy to one or two decimal places on most slide rules with the naked eye, and there are very large slide rules that are good for four decimal places, but it is impossible to do better than that. Generally speaking, analogue calculators are limited in their accuracy by the precision with which measurements of length, volume, or other physical quantities can be made. In fact, most big modern computers are digital: they operate with digits in much the same way a human calculator does. Still using blocks but taking the digital approach, we would represent the number 1 by one block, 2 by two blocks, and so on, and addition would involve counting up the blocks. In a digital machine, there is no question of measuring anything; the only limit to the accuracy of the basic arithmetic processes lies in the number of digits that the individual machine can manipulate. To put it briefly: an analogue calculator measures, while a digital computer counts.

One may wonder why an extremely high level of accuracy is needed. The first answer that comes to mind is that it is necessary in scientific and engineering applications. This is not really correct. A large modern computer does individual arithmetical operations that are accurate to many more decimal places than one ever needs in scientific work. This somewhat surprising point was emphasized by the late Professor John von Neumann in a set of published notes for a series of lectures— "The Computer and the Brain"—that he was preparing to deliver at Yale University just before his death, in 1957. Von Neumann wrote:

Why are such extreme precisions (like the digital [computer's] one part in a million million) at all necessary? . . . In most problems of applied mathematics and engineering the data are no better than a part in a thousand or a part in ten thousand and often they do not reach the level of a part in a hundred, and the answers are not required or meaningful with higher precisions. In chemistry, biology, or economics, or in other practical matters, the precision levels are usually even less exacting. It has nevertheless been the uniform experience in modern high-speed computing that even precision levels like a part in a hundred thousand are inadequate for a large part of important problems, and that digital machines with precision levels like one part in a million million are fully justified in practice. The reasons for this surprising phenomenon are interesting and significant. They are connected with the inherent structure of our present mathematical and numerical procedures.

Behind von Neumann's remarks is the fact that most numerical computations of the sort done on machines are necessarily approximate. The introduction of errors, even in a simple operation like multiplication, is inevitable, owing to the limited size of any given machine. As von Neumann put it:

Error, as a matter of normal operation and not solely as an accident attributable to some definite breakdown, creeps in, in the following manner. The absolutely correct product of two 10-digit numbers is a 20-digit number. If the machine is built to handle 10-digit numbers only it will have to disregard the last 10 digits of this 20-digit number and work with the first 10 digits alone. If, on the other hand, the machine can handle 20-digit numbers, then the multiplication of two such will produce 40 digits, and these again have to be cut down to 20, etc., etc.

The "rounding off" of numbers produces an error, and the error increases when the numbers are used in the next step of the computation, where again the result must be rounded off. In a long computation—and most computations done on a machine involve millions of arithmetical operations—the errors keep piling up, and that is why each part of the calculation must be done with the greatest possible accuracy. Von Neumann pointed out that to produce a final answer on a computer to an accuracy of one part in a thousand, it is necessary to perform the many intermediate steps to accuracies of the order of one part in a billion. That is the degree of accuracy that a typical modern digital computer can produce.

The abacus, which goes back at least to 450 B.C., was the first of the digital computers, and it is still undoubtedly the most widely used. It consists of a frame in which wires with beads strung on them are set in a harplike arrangement. The beads represent digits, and the wires represent "places"; the abacus, too, is limited in accuracy by its physical size. A skilled abacus operator can maneuver the beads on the place wires at enormous speed. A now almost legendary competition took place in 1946 between one Private Wood, of the American Occupation forces in Japan, and a Japanese clerk named Masturaki. The two men were given a number of arithmetic problems, with Mr. Masturaki using an abacus and Private Wood a hand-operated electric desk calculator. Mr. Masturaki won every time. (In an account of this contest, Dr. Bowden suggests that Mr. Masturaki may have had Klein-like abilities and may have been using the abacus simply as a prop.)

The first truly mechanical computer—an adding machine—seems to have been designed in 1642 by the French philosopher and mathematician Blaise Pascal. Pascal's device was very similar in principle to the modern desk adding devices, although these usually operate electrically instead of mechanically. The numbers, from 0 to 9, were engraved on a series of wheels. The first wheel on the right "stored" the integers 0 to 9, the second wheel the tens, the third the hundreds, and so on. To store, for example, 109 involved putting a 1 on the third wheel, a 0 on the second, and a 9 on the first. To add, say, 8 and 3, one stored the 8 on the first wheel and then turned the wheel through three places. This involved "carrying"—an operation that was done by a series of gears arranged so that they turned the next wheel. In 1671, Leibnitz

drew up a plan for a machine that could multiply
as well as add, and in 1694 a machine embodying
his design was actually built, although it did not
function very reliably.

At least part of the reason for the designing of
these early computers was the need to calculate
tables of the elementary functions, like sines, co-
sines, and logarithms, that arose again and again
in scientific and engineering calculations. It is
hard to realize now, when we have literally hundreds of such tables, that a few centuries ago one
of them could represent the lifework of a man.
Concerning the introduction of logarithms, which
were invented by the Scottish mathematician John
Napier around 1600 and were first tabulated in
1624 (to fourteen decimal places) by Henry
Briggs, Dr. Bowden writes:

> The introduction of logarithms by Napier
> and Briggs revolutionized ordinary comput-
> ing; our civilization, dependent as it is on nav-
> igation, surveying, and astronomy, could
> probably not have developed as it did without
> them. Briggs devoted his life to computing
> the logarithms which Napier had invented.
> Both men realized the importance of their
> work; when they were introduced in Edin-
> burgh, a friend related that they gazed at one
> another in speechless admiration for a quar-
> ter of an hour before the silence was broken.

One of the most grandiose of the early nonme-
chanical computing projects was initiated at the

end of the eighteenth century by the French First Republic. It was an elaborate program for the computation of mathematical tables by human beings. In a book entitled *Automatic Digital Computers,* Professor M. V. Wilkes, of Cambridge University, describes this almost Swiftian effort as follows:

> This project was organized on what we should now call production lines, and the staff were divided into three grades. First, there were some five or six mathematicians who decided the best mathematical methods and formulae to be used. Secondly, there were eight or ten computers who were competent to handle these formulae and to compute numerical values from them; their role was to compute "pivotal values," that is, selected values of the function spaced at five or ten times the interval required in the final table. Thirdly, there were computers of lower grade, nearly 100 in number, who understood only the elements of arithmetic, but who were able, by following rules laid down, to perform the final stage of the tabulation.

Professor Wilkes adds, "Seventeen folio volumes were computed for this project but were unfortunately never published. In 1820 the British government made a proposal that they should be published jointly but nothing came of it."

Anyone familiar with the use of modern computers will appreciate the similarities that must have existed between preparing instructions for the hundred arithmeticians and preparing a program for a machine. In fact, this similarity was not lost upon some of the mathematicians of the early nineteenth century, and certainly not upon the English mathematician Charles Babbage. Many remarkable men have contributed to the art of mechanical computation, but Babbage must surely be near the top of the list.

Babbage was born on December 26, 1792, at Totnes, in Devonshire. He was the son of a banker, and he eventually inherited a considerable fortune, which he used to finance scientific experiments. He taught himself mathematics as a boy, and when he went to Cambridge, in 1810, he found that he knew more algebra than his tutor. At Cambridge, he and some friends founded an organization called the Analytical Society, which was to "leave the world wiser than they found it." There are many accounts of Babbage's career, but one of the liveliest is Dr. Bowden's, which forms part of his essay on the history of computation. After describing Babbage's work on computers, Dr. Bowden writes:

Babbage was full of most ingenious ideas; for example he devised the method which during the last war became known as *Operational Research,* and applied it to an analysis of the pin-making industry. A similar analysis of the printing trade led to results which so offended his publishers that they refused to accept his books. He said, "Political economists have been reproached with too small a use of facts, and too large an employment of theory . . . let it not be feared that erroneous deductions may be made from recorded facts: the errors which arise from the absence of facts are far more numerous and durable than those which result from unsound reasoning respecting true data." This last sentence might be taken as the motto of operational research workers the world over. One of the most remarkable applications which he made of the method was to an analysis of the economics of the Post Office. He showed conclusively that the cost of collecting, "stamping," and delivering a letter was far greater than the cost of transporting it. He therefore suggested that operations of the Post Office should be simplified by the introduction of a flat rate of charges, which should be independent of the distance for which the letter had to be carried. It was as a result of these arguments of his that Sir Rowland Hill was encouraged to introduce the penny post a few years later. He studied the records of the Equitable Life Insurance Company, and published in 1824 the first comprehensive treatise on actuarial theory, and the first reliable "life tables." They were used both in England and Germany for half a century as the basis of the new and rapidly growing life-insurance business. . . . Babbage had a lifelong interest in inventing and in solving

codes and ciphers of all kinds; he made skele-
ton keys for "unpickable" locks; he devised
the method, which is now familiar to everyone, of identifying lighthouses by occulting
their lights in a rhythmical manner, and had
the mortification of seeing the scheme used
for the first time during the Crimean War—
by the Russians. . . .

[Babbage] set himself up in private practice as a consulting engineer and became
very interested in the development of the
railways. He was a friend of Sir Isambard
Brunel, chief engineer of the Great Western
Railway, and helped him by inventing the
dynamometer car, with which he could automatically measure and record the tractive
force of the locomotive and the irregularities
of the track. He used to run his special train
on Sundays, as there were fewer other trains
to compete with, but nevertheless the signal-
ling system was so bad that he often found
himself heading for another train coming
directly towards him on the same track. On
more than one occasion he owed his life to
the remarkable acuteness of his hearing,
which enabled him to get on to a siding and
avoid a head-on collision. He suggested the
use of the "cow catcher," and he devised
the first speedometer; he thought that there
should be one in the cab of every locomotive.
On one occasion he found himself on Han-
well viaduct on a flat car with no engine, and

by holding up a piece of cloth which he had with him he was able to *sail* across the viaduct. He remarked that he thought that he was the first man ever to do this, and it is likely that here again he established a record which will stand for many years to come.

Merely a glance at a portrait of Babbage indicates that he was not a man to put up with nonsense. One of his portraits hangs in the Science Museum in South Kensington; it shows him to have had a high, round forehead, sharp and wide-set eyes, a long, narrow mouth, and a stern, though not entirely humorless, look. He took vigorous swipes at most of the established institutions of his day, once remarking of the Royal Society, for instance, that he had tried to "rescue it from contempt in our own country, and ridicule in others," and he also carried on a lifelong polemic against organ-grinders and street musicians. Sometimes, his writings were testy and acid, but not always. After Lord Tennyson wrote "The Vision of Sin," Dr. Bowden tells us, Babbage sent this note to the poet:

SIR,

In your otherwise beautiful poem there is a verse which reads

> Every moment dies a man,
> Every moment one is born.

It must be manifest that if this were true, the population of the world would be at a standstill. In truth the rate of birth is slightly in

excess of that of death. I would suggest that
in the next edition of your poem you have it
read—

> Every moment dies a man,
> Every moment $1\frac{1}{16}$ is born.

Strictly speaking this is not correct, the actual figure is so long that I cannot get it into a
line, but I believe the figure $1\frac{1}{16}$ will be sufficiently accurate for poetry.

> I am, Sir, yours, etc.

Babbage seems to have been inspired to think
about computers by the image of the hundred
French arithmeticians executing, machinelike, the
commands of a few mathematicians. He puts
the year in which he first began thinking about
mechanical computers at 1812, and recalls in his
autobiography, *Passages from the Life of a Philosopher,* published in 1864: "One evening I was sitting in the rooms of the Analytical Society at Cambridge, my head leaning forward on the Table in a
kind of a dreamy mood, with a Table of logarithms
lying open before me. Another member coming
into the room, and seeing me half asleep called
out, 'Well, Babbage, what are you dreaming
about?' to which I replied, 'I am thinking that all
these Tables (pointing to the logarithms) might be
calculated by machinery.'"

It was not until several years later that Babbage
actually designed the first of his machines, the
Difference Engine, which was completed in 1822.
It was a relatively modest affair—basically an add-

ing machine that was specially designed for the computation of polynomials, such as x^2+x+41. Babbage's model worked to an accuracy of six decimal places and was actually used in the computation of tables. In his autobiography, Babbage gives an exceedingly lucid account of the principles of the Difference Engine. Lest the reader's enthusiasm for this difficult subject flag, Babbage encourages him with a quote from E. De Joncourt, an eighteenth-century professor of philosophy, who had published a celebrated table containing twenty thousand so-called triangular numbers (numbers like 1, 3, and 6 that can be arrayed in triangles $\quad .\quad .. \quad ...\quad$). De Joncourt wrote, "That sweet joy may arise from such contemplations cannot be denied. Numbers and lines have many charms, unseen by vulgar eyes, and only discovered to the unwearied and respectful souls of Art. In features the serpentine line (who starts not at the name) produces beauty and love; and in numbers, high powers, and humble roots, give soft delight. Lo! the raptured arithmetician! Easily satisfied, he asks no Brussels lace nor a coach and six. To calculate, contents his liveliest desires, and obedient numbers are within his reach."

As a next step, Babbage proposed to make a larger Difference Engine, which would be capable of working to an accuracy of twenty decimal places—no mean trick, even by modern standards. The British government contributed about seventeen thousand pounds toward its construction, but it was never completed. The engineering techniques of Babbage's time were not as far advanced as Babbage's imagination, and no one could make the levers and cogwheels with the precision he needed.

In 1833, Babbage conceived a new device, the Analytical Engine, which occupied him for the rest of his life, and which he never succeeded in building, either. The new engine represented a profound conceptual advance over the old one. The Difference Engine was designed to perform just the limited set of operations necessary in computing simple polynomials; the Analytical Engine was designed to perform any arithmetic operation at all and to string such operations together to solve, in principle, any conceivable arithmetic problem. In fact, the Analytical Engine would have had the sort of flexibility that modern machines have, though nowhere near their speed; Babbage envisioned that it might be able to perform about sixty additions a minute. All the operations were to be mechanical, and thus would involve the machinations of a vast collection of gears and cranks, which presumably were to be run on steam power.

The mechanical aspects of Babbage's engine, ingenious as they were, may seem archaic today, but his general conception of a computer, as we shall see, is not in the least archaic. His machine was to have four basic parts. There would have been what Babbage called the "store," in which the numerical data involved in a calculation would be placed. It would consist of columns of wheels, each bearing ten engraved digits. Babbage wanted the store to hold a thousand fifty-digit numbers. In trying to construct his store, he turned out thousands of superb mechanical drawings and a variety of new machine-shop techniques. The second basic part of his computer was to be the "mill"—the part in which arithmetical operations would be carried out, through the rotation of gears and wheels. Third, there was to be a device—essentially a collection of gears and levers—that could transfer numbers back and forth between the mill and the store. And, finally, there was a mechanism for getting numerical data in and out.

The best description of Babbage's proposed computer was given not by Babbage himself (for all his sharpness of tongue, he was, especially in later life, almost incapable of delivering a coherent account of the Analytical Engine) but by Ada Augusta, Countess of Lovelace, "the only daughter of the house and heart" of the poet Byron. Lady Lovelace, who was born in 1815, early showed a considerable aptitude for mathematics. When she was a child, she was taken with a group of Lady Byron's friends to see Babbage's Difference Engine, and one of them, Mrs. Augustus De Morgan, noted in her reminiscences, "While the rest of the party gazed at this beautiful instrument with the same sort of expression and feeling that some savages are said to have shown on first seeing a looking glass or hearing a gun, Miss Byron, young as she was, understood its working and saw the great beauty of the invention." Much of what is known about the principles of the Analytical Engine is the

result of Miss Byron's interest. In 1840, Babbage
gave some lectures in Turin, and in his audience
there was an Italian military engineer named L.
F. Menabrea, who was on the staff of the Royal
Academy at Turin; Menabrea was so impressed by
the lectures that he summarized them in an article, in French, which was published in Geneva in
1842. Later, Lady Lovelace translated this article
into English and annotated it. Her article, with its
annotations, is the best account available of the
technical aspects of Babbage's Analytical Engine.
Lady Lovelace described in great detail the method
that Babbage had devised for getting data in and
out of the machine. His plan was to take over the
method of punch cards that the French inventor
Jacquard had worked out for weaving patterns in
rugs. The pattern of punches was used to determine which threads would be woven into the rug
pattern at each pass of the shuttle, and the whole
process was based on whether certain rods in the
Jacquard loom did or did not encounter punches
in the cards. Patterns of great intricacy were made
on the Jacquard loom, and one of Babbage's most
prized possessions was a woven portrait of Jacquard himself, which had required the use of
twenty-four thousand cards. Babbage proposed to
make a very similar use of cards to run the Analytical Engine, the chief difference being that, as in
modern punch cards, the patterns of holes were to
correspond to mathematical symbols. As Lady
Lovelace put it, "We may say most aptly that the
Analytical Engine *weaves algebraic patterns* just

as the Jacquard-loom weaves flowers and leaves."

Anyone familiar with modern punch-card programming can only wonder at the sophistication of Babbage's ideas on the subject. In the first place, he saw clearly that by means of cards he could program his machine to do most of its operations automatically. Earlier computers had been largely manual, and the operator had had to intervene physically at every step of the way. Lady Lovelace wrote, "This engine surpasses its predecessors, both in the extent of the calculations which it can perform, in the facility, certainty and accuracy with which it can effect them, and in the absence of all necessity for the intervention of human intelligence *during the performance of its calculations*." Babbage also anticipated a number of specific elements of modern programming. For example, he recognized the utility of having special mathematical data stored in an external memory and accessible to the machine on call. If a certain logarithm was needed, the machine was to ring a bell and display at a window a card that would show which logarithm was needed. If the operator supplied the wrong value, the machine was to ring a louder bell. Today, when some quantity like a logarithm is needed, an electronic computer can ordinarily evaluate it afresh much faster than it can read the value from a stored table. This possibility was foreseen by Babbage. "It is an interesting question, which time only can solve, to know whether such Tables on cards will ever be required by the Engine," he wrote. "Tables are used for saving the time of continually computing individual numbers. But the computations to be made by the Engine are so rapid that it seems most probable that it will make shorter work by computing directly from proper formulae than by having recourse to its own Tables." Moreover, Babbage seems to have had a clear understanding of one of the most extraordinary and valuable abilities of automatic computers—the ability to perform conditional operations, such as those called for by the IF statement of FORTRAN. This is the statement that asks the machine to choose among steps, depending on what a previous step came up with—for instance, a positive or negative number. Since the outcome cannot be known prior to the calculation, either the machine must have some mechanism for making the decision and taking the appropriate next step or the operator must intervene in the calculation, thus slowing things down. Babbage's way of having his machine make this sort of decision was exceedingly ingenious, and is very similar in principle to the way modern machines make their decisions. To understand it, let us look at what happens when a larger number is subtracted from a smaller one:

$$
\begin{array}{r}
000\ 216 \\
-\ 000\ 317 \\
\hline
999\ 899
\end{array}
$$

The string of three zeros to the left of the 216 and 317 indicates that the size of the numbers we are considering is limited to six digits, and the array of 9s to the left of the 8 is the result of successive "borrowing" of 1s. If we were not limited to six-digit numbers, the string of 9s would extend indefinitely to the left. Ordinarily, one would write the result of this subtraction as —101. The number 999 899 is known as the "9s complement" of —101. It is easy to see that adding 999 899 to a number and throwing away the 1 to be carried at the end is equivalent to subtracting 101 from that number. For example:

$$
\begin{array}{r}
000\ 317 \\
-\ 000\ 101 \\
\hline
000\ 216
\end{array}
$$

And:

$$
\begin{array}{r}
000\ 317 \\
999\ 899 \\
\hline
000\ 216
\end{array}
$$

Many computers make use of the principle of complementing by 9s to perform subtractions by reducing them to addition.

Needless to say, any given machine can provide only a limited number of places, and Babbage made use of this fact in designing his Analytical Engine to make decisions. Suppose that it carried out a computation and got a negative answer. It would then produce a string of 9s to the left until it ran out of places. What Babbage did was to conceive of an extra place, which would be used not to register another 9 but to set in motion gears that could activate some other part of the computer, which would thereupon select an alternate set of punch cards. In other words, Babbage's machine could modify its course of action according to the outcome of previous calculations. Babbage described this process as "the Engine moving forward by eating its own tail," and he intended to use it in, among other things, programming the machine to perform cycles of operations. If one wanted to perform a certain set of operations, say, ten times, one would put the number 10 into a special register. Each time the operation was carried out, the machine would subtract a 1 from whatever number was left in that register. The next subtraction after the tenth would produce a negative number in the register, and a lever action set up by the string of 9s in the 9s complement of this number would be used to stop the cycle and get the machine started in a new phase of its calculation. This sequence of operations, which resembles that called for by the FORTRAN DO statement, is embodied in all modern computers.

Babbage spent nearly forty years trying to build the Analytical Engine. He could hardly think of anything else. In July, 1836, one of his friends, a mathematician named Mary Somerville, wrote to another friend, "Mr. Babbage is looking wretchedly and has been very unwell. I have done all I could to persuade him to leave town, but in vain. I do fear the machine will be the death of him, for certain I am that the human machine cannot stand that restless energy of mind." In 1842, the government stopped supporting his projects (Babbage described the responsible Chancellor of the Exchequer as "the Herostratus of Science," who, "if he escapes oblivion will be linked with the destroyer of the Ephesian temple"), and he and Lady Lovelace spent a considerable amount of time trying, without success, to invent a foolproof method of playing the horses in order to raise money for the Engine. Later on, Babbage invented a machine that could play ticktacktoe, and he thought for a time of building it and exhibiting it in carnivals. As he wrote in his autobiography:

> It occurred to me that if an automaton were made to play this game, it might be surrounded with such attractive circumstances that a very popular and profitable exhibition might be produced. I imagined that the machine might consist of the figures of two children playing against each other, accompanied by a lamb and a cock. That the child who won the game might clap his hands whilst the cock was crowing, after which, that the child who was beaten might cry and wring his hands whilst the lamb began bleating.
>
> Having fully satisfied myself of the power of making such an automaton, the next step was to ascertain whether there was any probability, if it were exhibited to the public, of its producing, in a moderate time, such a sum of money as would enable me to construct the

Analytical Engine. A friend, to whom I had at an early period communicated the idea, entertained great hopes of its pecuniary success. When it became known that an automaton could beat not merely children but even papa and mamma at a child's game, it seemed not unreasonable to expect that every child who heard of it would ask mamma to see it. On the other hand, every mamma, and some few papas, who heard of it would doubtless take their children to so singular and interesting a sight. I resolved, on my return to London, to make inquiries as to the relative productiveness of the various exhibitions of recent years, and also to obtain some rough estimate of the probable time it would take to construct the automaton, as well as some approximation to the expense.

It occurred to me that if half a dozen were made, they might be exhibited in three different places at the same time. Each exhibitor might then have an automaton in reserve in case of accidental injury. On my return to town I made the inquiries I alluded to, and found that the English machine for making Latin verses, the German talking-machine, as well as several others, were entire failures in a pecuniary point of view. I also found that the most profitable exhibition which had occurred for many years was that of the little dwarf, General Tom Thumb.

On considering the whole question, I arrived at the conclusion, that to conduct the affair to a successful issue it would occupy so much of my own time to contrive and execute the machinery, and then to superintend the working out of the plan, that even if successful in point of pecuniary profit, it would be too late to avail myself of the money thus acquired to complete the Analytical Engine.

By the time of Babbage's death, in 1871, the machine had eaten up much of his personal fortune. Some of its parts were actually constructed (largely by his son, H. P. Babbage), only to become museum curiosities, and a great many detailed drawings of other parts were made. His work was an enigma to most of his contemporaries, and since it was never completed, one cannot guess how they would have reacted to a large-scale computer. Lady Lovelace had some apprehensions about this, and she wrote a very wise commentary, which anticipated the sort of misunderstandings that the successful development of modern computers have given rise to. She warned:

It is desirable to guard against the possibility of exaggerated ideas that might arise as to the powers of the Analytical Engine. In considering any new subject, there is frequently a tendency, first to *overrate* what we find to be already interesting or remarkable; and, secondly, by a sort of natural reaction, to *undervalue* the true state of the case, when we do discover that our notions have surpassed those that were really tenable.

The Analytical Engine has no pretensions whatever to *originate* anything. It can do whatever we *know how to order it* to perform. It can *follow* analysis; but it has no power of *anticipating* any analytical relations or truths. Its province is to assist us in making *available* what we are already acquainted with.

At the time, however, Lady Lovelace's warning was somewhat premature. Babbage's work was forgotten until the nineteen-forties, when another generation of scientists and engineers, struggling anew with the problem of designing large-scale digital computers, came to realize that Babbage, with all his gears and cranks, had been there before them.

iii

-----------▶

ANY description of a modern digital computer can, broadly speaking, be divided into two parts. One has to do with the machine's "hardware"—its specific electronic components and circuits—and the other has to do with its logical design; that is, the organization of the available components, whatever they may be. In practice, of course, the two aspects are connected; it would not be of much use to design a machine whose circuitry was beyond the scope of existing technology. The circuitry of any modern computer is extremely complex, and to understand it in any depth requires a good deal of expertise in electronics and electrical engineering. However, one can understand much about the logical organization of the machines without knowing how all of the parts work in detail. In fact, Babbage's Engine had no electrical parts and yet its logical organization has a lot in common with that of the modern machines. Modern electronic technology has produced computer parts more efficient than even Babbage imagined, but they are put together in units he would certainly have found familiar.

All computers consist of four basic units. In the first place, there must be some mechanism for getting data and instructions into the machine and for getting answers out—the link, that is, between the machine and the human programmer. Today, there are a variety of methods for establishing this link. For instance, to consider just input, data may be recorded on punch cards, much as Babbage envisioned, or on magnetic tape, which can be fed into the computer and "read" by it electronically. In either case, the numbers and letters in the programmer's language are translated into coded patterns, and the coded patterns, in turn, are translated by the electronics of the machine into patterns of electrical pulses. These patterns must be stored somewhere in the machine until they are needed, and thus the second basic element in the machine is Babbage's "store"—or memory, as it is called today. In most modern machines, the memory that stores numbers consists of a great many tiny magnets that respond to the patterns of electrical pulses. In the third place, the machine must have some arrangement for manipulating stored numbers—the "mill," or, in the modern phrase, the arithmetic unit. For example, if two numbers are to be added, there must be a part of the machine in which the actual addition can take place. Today's arithmetic unit is a complex of special circuits designed to combine the patterns of electrical pulses corresponding to the individual numbers into new patterns of pulses, corresponding to the results of the arithmetical operation. Finally, there must be an element that controls the entire sequence of operations. This control unit—another complex of special circuits —not only arranges for numbers to be brought into and out of the memory but guides the whole sequence of arithmetic operations, and it does all this on the basis of a program drawn up by a human programmer. It is one of the triumphs of modern electronics that circuits that do all these things have been designed and produced, and it is a tribute to Babbage that he envisioned how the same things could have been done by a collection of gears and wheels and levers.

The first large, modern calculators that were actually built were of the analogue type—machines in which the arithmetic operations are carried out in terms of physical measurements. (The Analytical Engine would have been a digital computer.)

The modern era of mechanical computation began about 1925, at the Massachusetts Institute of Technology, when Dr. Vannevar Bush and some associates made a large-scale analogue calculator. It had electric motors, but otherwise it was entirely mechanical. The quantities being computed were represented by the number of degrees through which certain gears had rotated, and this meant that the accuracy of the computations was limited by the precision with which the angles could be measured. In 1935, the M.I.T. group began designing a second model, which introduced, along with other improvements, an electrical method for measuring the angles. This model was completed in 1942, but the fact was kept secret until the end of the war, because the Bush machines were extensively used for the computation of artillery firing tables. (A rumor was deliberately circulated that it had been impossible to finish the new model.) Computing the tables involved solving "ordinary" differential equations—equations with just one variable—and the machines were reasonably fast, by human standards; solving a typical equation, which might have taken a human computer a week, took the machines about half an hour. However, as is true of all analogue calculators, there were intrinsic limitations to their flexibility. Most problems in physics and engineering involve the solution of partial differential equations—equations with many variables—something entirely beyond the capacity of the Bush calculators.

In 1937, Howard Aiken, who is a professor of

information technology at the University of Miami, in Florida, and president of Howard Aiken Industries, Inc., with headquarters in New York, began work at Harvard on his Ph.D. thesis in physics. The theoretical aspects of the thesis involved the solution of so-called nonlinear ordinary differential equations, which could be done only by means of numerical approximation, and the computations needed to reach these approximate solutions proved to be extremely long. Aiken began considering possible methods of doing the computations on machines, and he soon invented a machine that would evaluate simple polynomials. After a year or two, during which he invented variations on this machine that would solve more complex kinds of problems, it occurred to him that all these machines were, in their logical organization, essentially identical, and he started thinking about the construction of a single general-purpose machine, capable of dealing with any of the problems. He was able to get support for his project from the International Business Machines Corporation, and in 1939 work on the machine—the Automatic Sequence Controlled Calculator, Mark I, as it became known—was begun at I.B.M. in a collaboration between Aiken and four I.B.M. engineers named J. W. Bryce, C. D. Lake, B. M. Durfee, and F. E. Hamilton. The Mark I was completed in 1944, and was put into operation at Harvard. About three years after Professor Aiken began working on computers, he discovered Babbage. He was startled to find that he and Babbage had been preoccupied by the same problems. As Professor Aiken put it recently, "If Babbage had lived seventy-five years later, I would have been out of a job." In fact, the operating manual of the Mark I begins with a quotation from Babbage's book: "If, unwarned by my example, any man shall succeed in constructing an engine embodying in itself the whole of the executive department of mathematical analysis . . . I have no fear of leaving my reputation in his charge, for he alone will be able fully to appreciate the nature of my efforts and the value of their results." When Professor Aiken first came across these lines, he felt that Babbage was addressing him personally from the past.

The Mark I was designed to perform computations by following automatically—that is, without manual intervention on the part of the machine operator—a sequence of instructions that had been prepared for it by a programmer. The instructions were fed into it on a punched paper tape, and the numbers on which the instructions were to operate were stored in registers. One might wish to give the machine an instruction like this: "Take a number out of Register 32, put the number into Register 64, and then read the next line on the coding tape." This instruction would appear in the form of the sequence of numbers 32647, in which the 7 was the code for instructing the machine to read the next line, while 32 and 64 referred to the "addresses"—the particular registers—in which the numbers had been stored. Computations were broken down into small steps, and each step had to be expressed in terms of the primitive instructions that the machine could follow. As machine computations generally involve an enormous number of steps, the programmer had to go about writing down meticulously a very long sequence of such instructions—a tedious business.

The Mark I was electro-mechanical; the basic operations were performed by mechanical parts that were controlled electrically. Typical of these was the ordinary telephone relay—a device in which a metal bar attached to a spring can be raised by the pulling action of an electromagnet. When the magnet is turned off, the bar falls, completing a circuit. Such relays were used not only in the Mark I but also in some interesting smaller computing devices that were under development at about the same time at Bell Telephone Laboratories, under the direction of Dr. George R. Stibitz, a mathematician there. The Mark I used about three thousand of the relays. Like most mechanical devices, and unlike the basic electronic devices of today, they were relatively large and slow. Each relay was about an inch long, and could be opened or closed in about a hundredth of a second. It took some four and a half seconds for the Mark I to multiply two twenty-three-digit numbers—the largest numbers it could handle. What with its relays and other mechanical parts, the Mark I's calculating was audible. As a student at Harvard, I used to drop in now and then and have a look at it. It was situated in a red brick structure just behind the physics building, and when it was working, one could go in and listen to the gentle clicking of the relays, which sounded like a roomful of ladies knitting.

It would not be completely unreasonable to say that by the time the Mark I machine went into operation, it was almost obsolete. (This is not meant as a reflection on the machine; it operated for more than fifteen years and turned out quantities of mathematical tables that are still being used.) However, about a year earlier, at the Moore School of Electrical Engineering of the University of Pennsylvania, Dr. J. Presper Eckert, an electrical engineer, and Dr. John Mauchly, a physicist, had begun work on the ENIAC—the Electronic Numerical Integrator and Calculator. This was the first electronic computer, for instead of relays and other semi-mechanical devices Eckert and Mauchly used vacuum tubes. The current in a tube is composed of flowing electrons, and changing the tube's state involves stopping or starting the flow. These electrons have a tiny mass as compared to the mass of the iron bar that has to be moved when a telephone relay is switched. In a vacuum tube, very strong electrical forces are brought to bear on the electrons, giving them very high accelerations in extremely short times, and the state of the tube can be changed in about a millionth of a second. By the time the first model of the ENIAC was ready for operation, early in 1946, it was by far the most complex electronic device in the world.

A large factor in the decision to build the ENIAC

was military pressure. In 1943, the Moore School and the Aberdeen Proving Ground, in Maryland, were conducting a joint project involving the computation of artillery firing tables for the Army. The Moore School contingent, which used a Bush analogue computer and employed a hundred girls to do hand computations as a necessary adjunct to the machine operations, was under the command of a young first lieutenant in the Army Ordnance Corps named Herman H. Goldstine, who had been an assistant professor of mathematics at the University of Michigan before the war. When I went to see Dr. Goldstine, who is director of mathematical research at the I.B.M. Thomas J. Watson Research Center, in Yorktown Heights, he told me that the results produced by the hundred girls and the machine were not very satisfactory—that, indeed, by the time Eckert and Mauchly began work on the ENIAC the situation had become "desperate." Back in the summer of 1942, Mauchly had written an informal report on the possibilities of making an electronic computer. In the course of things, the report got lost. Early in 1943, Mauchly and Eckert reconstructed it from a secretary's shorthand notes, and Eckert added an appendix containing some explicit suggestions as to how Mauchly's ideas might be embodied in electronic hardware. Dr. Goldstine, who was serving as liaison officer between the Moore School group and Army Ordnance, decided to try to get the backing of Army Ordnance for the project. On April 9, 1943, there was a meeting—attended by, among other people,

Colonel Leslie E. Simon, then director of the Ballistic Research Laboratory at Aberdeen, and Professor Oswald Veblen, of the Institute for Advanced Study, at Princeton, who was one of this country's most distinguished mathematicians—at which the potentialities of the ENIAC were discussed. After hearing about the machine, Veblen stood up and said, "Simon, back that thing!" The Army backed it.

Strangely, there was nothing in the completed ENIAC that could not have been put together at least a decade before the war, if anyone had had the incentive to do it. Early in 1962, Harold Bergstein, who was then editor of a magazine called *Datamation*, interviewed Eckert and Mauchly. Part of the interview, as published, went this way:

BERGSTEIN: Since the ENIAC was a direct result of your efforts and government money during World War Two, when would you speculate that the [electronic] digital computer might have been invented (a) if there had been no war, and (b) if there were no Eckert and Mauchly to invent it?

ECKERT: I think you certainly would have had computers about the same time. There are a lot of things which cannot linger long without being born. Actually, calculus was invented simultaneously by two different individuals. It's been the history of invention over and over again that when things are kind of ready for invention, then somebody does it.

What puzzles me most is that there wasn't anything in the ENIAC in the way of components that wasn't available 10 and possibly 15 years before. . . . The ENIAC could have been invented 10 or 15 years earlier and the real question is, why wasn't it done sooner?

MAUCHLY: In part, the demand wasn't there. The demand, of course, is a curious thing. People may need something without knowing that they need it.

In the summer of 1944, the late Professor John von Neumann, who was then a consultant to the group engaged on the atomic-bomb project at Los Alamos, started working in the field of electronic computing; his job at Los Alamos was to find techniques for performing the immensely involved numerical computations that were necessary in the design of nuclear weapons. By any standard, von Neumann, was one of the most creative and versatile scientists of the twentieth century. He began his career as a chemical engineer, and though he turned to pure mathematics and theoretical physics, he retained a profound feeling for engineering practicalities. Indeed, his contributions to computing machines ranged from articulating the general logical theory of their design to working out the details of the construction of specific circuit elements. Von Neumann was born in Budapest, and after receiving his Doctor's degree, in 1926, he was a *Privatdozent* first in Berlin and then in Hamburg. He came to the United States in 1930 and spent three years at Princeton University. Then, in 1933, he became one of the first permanent members of the Institute for Advanced Study (Einstein was another of the original members), and he remained there until the summer of 1955, when he was appointed to the Atomic Energy Commission. A great deal of von Neumann's work in mathematics was inspired by problems that arose in the mathematical formulation of physics. He was able to take apparently unrelated concepts in theoretical physics and organize them into beautifully compact logical structures. Furthermore, he was one of the formulators of the "'theory of games." This is the mathematical study of the strategy for winning very complex games. Such games can serve as models for economic or military strategy. A book that von Neumann wrote with the economist Oskar Morgenstern, *Theory of Games and Economic Behavior,* is a fundamental contribution to the field of operational research. Von Neumann had a phenomenal capacity for doing mental computations of all kinds. His thought processes were extremely fast, and often he would see through to the end of someone's argument almost before the speaker had got out the first few sentences. Recently, one of von Neumann's colleagues said in affectionate explanation of von Neumann's power, "You see, Johnny wasn't human. But after living with humans for so long he learned how to do a remarkable imitation of one."

During the summer of 1944, Goldstine ran into von Neumann in a railroad station near the Aberdeen Proving Ground. Von Neumann was also serving as a consultant for Aberdeen, and he and Goldstine knew each other slightly. Goldstine told von Neumann that the Moore School group appeared to be well on its way to building an electronic computer that would be about a thousand times as fast as any of the existing electromechanical ones. Von Neumann immediately became much excited about the idea. As Goldstine has put it, "Once Johnny saw what we were up to, he jumped into electronic computers with both feet." Von Neumann's enthusiasm for the prospect of electronic computers can be fully appreciated only if one attempts to visualize the degree of complexity of the sort of calculations that were necessary in nuclear weapons design. In a fascinating description of von Neumann's life and work which appeared in the May 1958 issue of the *Bulletin of the American Mathematical Society*, Dr. Stanislaw Ulam of Los Alamos, a close friend, and a collaborator of von Neumann's on weapons-design work, wrote, "After one discussion in which we outlined the course of such a calculation von Neumann turned to me and said, 'Probably in its execution we shall have to perform more elementary arithmetical steps than the total in all the computations performed by the human race heretofore.' We noticed, however, that the total number of multiplications made by the school children of the world in course of a few years sensibly exceeded that of our problem."

Von Neumann began an active collaboration

with the Moore School group. At this time there were a good many exchanges of ideas among the members of the group, and it is almost impossible to give a completely coherent account of who invented what. In any event, certain aspects of the work culminated in a series of reports written by von Neumann and Goldstine, with the help in the first report of Arthur W. Burks, who is a member of the Philosophy Department of the University of Michigan. That first report, entitled "Preliminary Discussion of the Logical Design of an Electronic Computing Instrument," appeared on June 28, 1946. Curiously, although it has turned out to be one of the basic papers in the electronic-computing field, it was until recently published only in the form of a U.S. Army Ordnance Department report.

Perhaps the most important idea discussed in this paper is that of "the stored program." To understand what this means, it is helpful to return to the ENIAC. In the ENIAC, as in any other computer, there was a memory for storing numbers. These numbers were manipulated by instructions that were themselves stored in electrical circuits in another part of the machine. Before starting on a given problem, one had to figure out each of the necessary instructions and hook up the appropriate circuits by hand—an operation that was something like plugging up connections on a telephone switchboard. In fact, plugging up a problem on the ENIAC sometimes took several people several days and involved making hundreds of wired connections. In a stored-program machine, certain common and basic operations are built into the circuitry. Each of these operations is given a number, and the machine is so arranged that an operation can be called for by its number. The programmer can draw up his program in terms of these numbers, which will then be stored in the memory along with the rest of the numerical data. It must be made clear in the program which addresses in the memory contain instructions and which contain data. Machine operation is divided into two kinds of time cycles—"instruction" cycles and "execution" cycles. During an instruction cycle, the control unit interprets any number brought into it as an instruction, and the instruction is "decoded," which means that the built-in circuitry needed for carrying it out is activated. During the execution cycle, the machine executes the instruction.

Generally, the stored-program machine proceeds automatically from one programmed instruction to the next. However, the sequence can be varied by what is called "conditional transfer" of control. In a conditional transfer, the machine is instructed to determine the sign of a number that it has computed and that has been put into the "accumulator"—a special register in the control unit. To give an example: If this number is positive, the machine simply takes the next instruction in the sequence; if it is negative, the machine will take an instruction out of sequence, from an address in the memory that is specified in the program. Thus, a conditional transfer enables the machine to change the flow of its computation as it goes along. This ability is a basic feature of all modern digital computers.

Stored-program computers have an almost unlimited flexibility. Von Neumann wrote:

> Since the orders that exercise the entire control are in the memory, a higher degree of flexibility is achieved than in any previous mode of control. Indeed, the machine, under control of its orders, can extract numbers (or orders) from the memory, process them (as numbers!), and return them to the memory (to the same or other locations); i.e., it can change the contents of the memory—indeed this is its normal *modus operandi*. Hence it can, in particular, change the orders (since these are in the memory!)—the very orders that control its actions. Thus all sorts of sophisticated order-systems become possible, which keep successively modifying themselves and hence also the computational processes that are likewise under their control. . . . Although all of this may sound farfetched and complicated, such methods are widely used and very important in recent machine-computing—or, rather, computation-planning practice.

In 1945, some time before the ENIAC went into operation, the Moore School group began working on the design and construction of a stored-program computer, to be called the EDVAC, or Electronic Discrete Variable Automatic Computer. It was completed in 1950 at the Aberdeen Proving Ground—and was still in operation there as late as 1962—but not by the original group, which had split up after the war, von Neumann returning to Princeton along with Goldstine, while Eckert and Mauchly began designing machines commercially. (The first stored-program computer actually completed was the EDSAC—for Electronic Delay Storage Automatic Calculator—built at the mathematical laboratory of the University of Cambridge. It went into operation in May, 1949.) UNIVAC I—for Universal Automatic Computer—the first commercial stored-program computer, was built for Sperry-Rand by Eckert and Mauchly, and upon its completion, in 1951, was delivered to the Bureau of the Census. (In October, 1963, UNIVAC I was officially retired to the Smithsonian Institution after more than seventy-three thousand hours of operational use.) At Princeton, von Neumann supervised the construction of an experimental computer that embodied his ideas on machine organization. It went into operation in 1952. Paul Armer, of the Rand Corporation, in Santa Monica, wrote in a recent issue of *Datamation:* "The machine (variously known as the I.A.S., or Princeton, or von Neumann machine) was constructed and copied (never exactly), and the copies were copied. One version of it, built at Rand, was affectionately called JOHNNIAC (over von Neumann's objections). Most of the copies are still in operation, although the [original] I.A.S. machine now has its place in history at the Smithsonian."

Another very important idea that was discussed in the von Neumann, Goldstine, Burks paper is the application of the binary number system to computers. In daily life, we are accustomed to doing arithmetic with the decimal system, which employs the ten digits from 0 to 9. In fact, most of us are so used to this system that we find it hard to appreciate that its use in arithmetic is quite arbitrary. In the reckoning of time, there are residues of other systems; the number of hours in the day is counted by twelves (the duodecimal system), and the number of seconds in the minute by sixties (the sexagesimal system). The predominance of the decimal system undoubtedly has to do with the fact that the best-known counting instrument of all—the fingers on one's hands—operates by tens. Much the simplest system, though, is the binary. In it, all numbers are built up from the digits 0 and 1. In the binary system, as in the decimal system, the first digit is 0 and the next is 1, but there the similarity stops. To represent 2 in the binary system we must take the next-largest number that can be made from 0 and 1, which is 10. The 3 is represented in binary by 11, and so on, with the result that the numbers between 0 and 9 are reëxpressed like this:

Decimal	Binary
0	0
1	1
2	10
3	11
4	100
5	101
6	110
7	111
8	1000
9	1001

To construct the next number on the list, a 1 is added to the previous number using the rules $1 + 0 = 1$ and $1 + 1 = 10$ and "carrying" whenever necessary. This number system may seem strange at first, but one soon gets used to it, and it turns out to be far and away the most sensible number system to use in computers.

One reason for this is that the basic electronic components of a computer are "bi-stable"; that is, they have an intrinsically binary character. A switch can be open or closed; a pulse can be present or absent; a vacuum tube can be on or off. All these devices thus have just two stable modes of operation, which can be made to correspond to the 1 and 0 of the binary system. Therefore, if an electronic machine were to store its data in decimal, it would need ten vacuum tubes, or other bi-stable devices, to represent the ten possible values for any one decimal place. Indeed, the ENIAC did use the decimal system in storing numbers. Although some applications of binary arithmetic had been made in the earlier relay machines—Dr. Stibitz built a binary adder as early as 1937—it was only with the advent of electronic machines, that the use of binary storage and arithmetic became common practice. The bi-stable electronic devices can be used to store binary directly, and essentially all the machines that have followed the ENIAC have made use of binary numbers throughout. The use of binary greatly simplifies arithmetical processes in the machine. Binary addition, for example, is very simple to translate in terms of electric circuits. 1+0=1 means that when a particular circuit, designed for adding, is fed one pulse, corresponding to a 1, along with no pulse, corresponding to a 0, it responds by producing one pulse, corresponding to a 1. Multiplication in binary is equally easy. To see this, we have only to multiply 2 and 3 in binary—which means that we multiply the binary numbers 10 and 11:

$$
\begin{array}{r}
11 \\
10 \\
\hline
00 \\
11 \\
\hline
110
\end{array}
$$

The number 110, as we have seen, is the binary equivalent of 6. It is evident from this example that multiplying the 11 by the 0 in the 10 produces just zeros, while multiplying it by the 1 in the 10 produces the number 11 again. This is characteristic of binary multiplication, and makes the designing of multiplying circuits much simpler than it would be if the multiplication were done in decimal, in which each place in the product may have any of the ten values between 0 and 9.

In the parlance of information theory, the fact that a bi-stable device is on or off is said to constitute a "bit" of information. Thus, it takes at most four bits of information to store a decimal digit in binary. (For example, to store the number 8, which is 1000 in binary, clearly requires four on-off registers, while the number 4, which is 100 in binary, requires three on-off units.) In the I.B.M. 7090 computer, to take a typical modern machine, information is stored in the memory in units of "words," each containing thirty-six bits. The 7090 can store approximately thirty-three thousand words, which means that it can store about thirty-three thousand ten-digit numbers. Babbage planned to store in his Engine a thousand fifty-digit numbers. This represents an amount of information not very different from the amount that modern machines actually store.

The ENIAC was not only the first fully electronic computer ever built but also just about the largest. It occupied roughly eighteen hundred square feet. Subsequent computers that have proved vastly more powerful and efficient nonetheless take up much less space. The reason for this lies in the invention of several new electronic components, which perform the same functions as the older vacuum tubes but are much smaller and more rugged. As far as computers go, the most important of these devices—they are referred to as "solid-state" devices—are the transistor and the magnetic core. The transistor was first developed in 1948 by three physicists at Bell Telephone Laboratories—J. Bardeen, W. H. Brattain, and W. Shockley, who shared the 1956 Nobel Prize in physics for their work on it. A typical transistor consists of a crystal of silicon or germanium. It conducts electric current in much the same way as a vacuum tube, but it operates "cold." The electrons in a vacuum tube are made to "flow" when part of the tube is heated. They are boiled off the hot metal and then made to flow in a current by suitable electric fields. In a transistor, the electrons flow when a voltage is applied. No heating is involved, and hence there is nothing to burn out. Moreover, most transistors are so small that a magnifying glass is needed to study them, whereas a vacuum tube capable of performing a comparable function has a volume of at least a few cubic inches. In the 7090, there are forty-four thousand transistors.

In a computer memory, the magnetic cores are tiny rings of magnetic material, made by pressing the powdered material and baking it in an oven. They, too, are extremely small compared to a vacuum tube; typically, the diameter of the ring is a few hundredths of an inch. The magnetic material in the core can be oriented clockwise or counterclockwise by exposure to electric pulses. Cores, like transistors, operate cold, so they very rarely have to be changed during the operating lifetime of a machine. The use of cores as elements in computer memories dates back to around 1950. In the memory of the 7090, the cores are strung on wires that are arranged in a framework in an almost tennis-racket formation; there are seventy-two of the frames, each containing 16,384 cores strung along the wires; in all, the memory contains 1,179,648 cores. Four wires pass through each core. Three of the wires are used to change the magnetic orientation of the core by passing electrical pulses through it—in other words, to "write" information into the core. The fourth wire is used to "read out" that information. Typically, as soon as the information contained in a core is read out, the core is reset so that the information it contained will be available for the next reading. In the 7090, the read-write operation takes about two-millionths of a second to complete.

Ultimately, the hardware of a computing machine can respond only to electrical pulses. In the stored-program machine, coded numbers can be used to activate different parts of the electronic circuitry. In the 7090, for instance, there are about two hundred such coded operations. As an example of how they are used, we can put together a few of them in carrying out the addition of two numbers—a very simple machine operation. Suppose the numbers to be added are stored in Ad-

dresses 201 and 202 of the memory. The first step
in the process is to take the number in, say, Address 201 and deposit it in the accumulator. This
operation is designated by the pair of numbers
+500 201, in which +500 stands for the operation of clearing, or emptying, the accumulator and
depositing in it the number stored in Address 201.
The "sign" of a number can be specified in the
memory, and in the 7090 the number +500
stands for an entirely different operation from
−500. The clear-and-deposit operation is actually
known to the programmer as "clear and add," or
CLA, which is easier to remember than +500.
Next comes the message +400 202; it tells the
machine to add the number in Address 202 to
whatever is in the accumulator—in this case, of
course, the former contents of Address 201. The
mnemonic for this operation is ADD. The next step
is to take the sum and store it in another location
—let's call it Address 301—where it can be available for use in some other part of the computation. This would be indicated by +601 301, where
+601 is the code for STO, or "store." Finally, this
phase of the computation might be ended with the
instruction +000 217, instructing the machine to
"halt and transfer"—the mnemonic for this being
HTR. The "transfer" part of the instruction indicates to the machine that when it is started again,
control will be transferred to some instruction lo-
cated in Address 217. Thus, the whole sequence
would look schematically like:

+ 500	201
+ 400	202
+ 601	301
+ 000	217

Machine instructions like +500 and +601, or even CLA and HTR, are a far cry from human language. Ideally, one would like to draw up a program for solving a problem in, say, English, leave the room, and let the machine translate the English into machine language, translate the machine language into electronics, do its computation, and print out the result in English. One of the most striking facts about modern computer operation is that for a wide class of problems this is very nearly possible. It has come about through the development of several remarkable languages that serve to bridge the gap between machine language and the language of the user. The development of such languages has been taking place over the last decade, and by now there are several. Most of them have somewhat odd-sounding names, like ALGOL (Algorithmic Language) and COBOL (Common Business Oriented Language), or faintly humorous ones, like SALE (Simple Algebraic Language for Engineers) and JOVIAL (Jules' Own Version of the International Algebraic Language). The first of them was FORTRAN (Formula Translation), and it has become an important tool in doing scientific computation.

The task of designing a computer language like

FORTRAN is a very complex one. In the first place, an analysis must be made of processes and steps that occur frequently in the solution of mathematical problems—operations like conditional transfer. To direct the computer to perform such operations usually requires several machine-language instructions. FORTRAN consists of set phrases— for instance, IF, indicating a conditional transfer —which the programmer must fit together so that they express a method of solving his problem. These phrases must be translated into machine language, and the inventors of FORTRAN had to design a master translating program, itself written in machine language, which would instruct the machine to do this translation. The beauty of FOR-TRAN is that once it and the translating program have been set up, the user of the machine can for many purposes forget about the machine-language instructions altogether. He can write his program in terms of the IFS and DOS of FORTRAN, and let the translating program do the job of producing the machine language. The FORTRAN phrases have been so chosen that writing a program in them is not immensely different from the way one might write out such a program in English.

By 1954, when an I.B.M. team began work in New York on what turned out to be FORTRAN, there had been at least two attempts to construct programming languages. J. Halcombe Laning and Neal Zierler, who were working with the Whirlwind (an early vacuum-tube stored-program computer built at M.I.T. and completed in 1951), had

formulated a translating program that accepted
mathematical or algebraic statements reasonably
similar to those of FORTRAN and produced
machine-language programs. These programs
were quite inefficient compared to the sort that
could be written by a human computer, and the
system was not used very often. Also, H. Rutis-
hauser, of the Eidgenössische Technische Hoch-
schule, in Zurich, had produced a fairly complete
language for scientific computing, but the computer he had available was too small to use for
translating. In fact, most of the people involved
with computers in the mid-nineteen-fifties did not
consider such translating programs a very practical possibility. The reason was partly that the job
had never been done, and partly that even if it
were done, the programs that a machine could produce for itself would, it was felt, be slower and less
efficient than the ones a skilled human programmer could produce for it. As one of the men active
in computers at that time has told me, "In those
days, when we talked of the users of a computing
machine, we had in mind the trained programmer,
who did the programming for the *real* user—the
man who wanted his problem solved. It seemed
clear that the work of a trained programmer could
beat a machine-constructed program, and it didn't
occur to most people that with automatic translators the real user could learn to code his own problem and become his own programmer."

As things turned out, the language that the
I.B.M. group developed was so skillfully con-

structed that the programs it produces are usually competitive in efficiency with those of a human programmer. In the group's first report on the completed FORTRAN, which appeared in 1957, it cited a case history, with an appropriate caution:

A brief case history of one job done with a system seldom gives a good measure of its usefulness, particularly when the selection is made by the authors of the system. Nevertheless, here are the facts about a rather simple but sizable job. The programmer attended a one-day course on FORTRAN and spent some more time referring to the manual. He then programmed the job in four hours, using 47 FORTRAN statements. These were compiled [translated] by the 704 [an ancestor of the 7090] in six minutes, producing about 1000 instructions. He ran the program and found the output incorrect. He studied the output and was able to localize his error in a FORTRAN statement he had written. He rewrote the offending statement, recompiled, and found that the resulting program was correct. He estimated that it might have taken three days to code this job by hand, plus an unknown time to de-bug it, and that no appreciable increase in speed of execution would have been achieved thereby.

Roughly, it takes between four and twenty machine-language instructions to cover what is conveyed by each FORTRAN phrase. The translating program itself consists of more than twenty-five thousand lines of machine language, and took the original group almost two and a half years to design; this program has been put on magnetic tape, and every computer installation that uses FORTRAN has a copy of the tape. The first FORTRAN translating system was designed specifically for the I.B.M. 704—one of the first computers to use a magnetic-core memory. As the machines got faster and more powerful, it was possible to enlarge and refine the language, and by 1962 FORTRAN had gone through four revisions. It was extremely important that each revised version should retain enough elements of the prior versions so that programs written in the older language could readily be accommodated to the new machines. Computer programs are costly to develop (a 1961 estimate in *Business Week* indicated that since 1950 computer users had invested more than two billion dollars in the development of programs) and usually reflect the accumulated experience of a variety of machine users. Among users, it has become a custom to send program corrections and improvements to the computer manufacturers, and thanks to this custom an enormous lore of programming technology has been built up around FORTRAN. All this would be lost if the language should be abruptly modified. (In general, computer programs are not patentable. I.B.M. could have registered the name FORTRAN, although not the compiling program itself. The company felt that it would be to everyone's advantage to have the language used as widely as possible, so no attempt was made to register the name.)

Though FORTRAN is not the only computer language, it is the one that is most widely used for scientific and engineering purposes. Not only are there foreign-language versions of the instruction manuals for using FORTRAN but there is even a French-language FORTRAN, which contains words like LIRE, FAIRE, and ALLER, which the French FORTRAN translating program enables the machines to translate into machine language. Mostly, however, computers are used not for scientific and engineering purposes but for "data processing"— routine but essential tasks like making out payrolls and keeping inventories straight. The people who use them in this way have seldom had scientific or mathematical training, and while FORTRAN can be used by people without specialized scientific training, it is a highly compact and somewhat abstract language. Therefore, as soon as the value of FORTRAN had been demonstrated, there was a large-scale effort, involving many computer manufacturers, to develop a language that would be more directly suited to business purposes. Fearing a consequent Tower of Babel, the Defense Department, a very important consumer of computer time, called a conference at the University of Pennsylvania in 1958 of both manufacturers and users to study the feasibility of developing a unified business-oriented language. Out of this conference and various study groups that succeeded it came COBOL. One of the features of COBOL is the high incidence of terms like "WAREHOUSE" and "PART NUMBER." The machine can translate whole sentences like "SORT INVENTORY FILE ON ASCENDING KEY WAREHOUSE PART NUMBER." Most of the major computer manufacturers have models that translate COBOL, and the Defense Department has indicated that it intends to use computers for data-processing applications only if they have COBOL translators. It is possible to do scientific problems with COBOL, but the language lacks the compact, mathematical quality of FORTRAN. An attempt is now being made to prepare a standardized FORTRAN, to be used on all scientific computers. American Standards Association, Inc., an outfit that helps set standards in all kinds of industries, has been working with a group of manufacturers and users of computing machines to arrange for uniform standards for future computers. The association has a FORTRAN committee, headed by W. P. Heising, of I.B.M., and Mr. Heising and his committee have been setting up a minimal-standard FORTRAN, which all large-scale scientific computers will be equipped to handle. While manufacturers are not legally bound by the agreements reached through American Standards, the fact that the larger manufacturers are all involved probably means that in the future most scientific computing in the United States will be done in FORTRAN.

My own modest brush with FORTRAN gave me a good deal of respect for the power and ingenuity of the language, and when I decided to learn more about the history of computing and computing machines, I asked the people at I.B.M. if I might talk with some members of the team that devised FORTRAN. In time, I went to Yorktown Heights to see two of them—John W. Backus and Irving Ziller. Both Backus and Ziller got into computing in the early nineteen-fifties, almost immediately after leaving college. In the summer of 1954, Backus, who was doing programming research for I.B.M., requested the company's support for work on what was to become FORTRAN. The support was granted, and he was able to put together a small group, which gradually grew into a thirteen-man team. Backus said that when he and his associates began, they didn't have the vaguest idea of how the project was going to work out in detail; although, from a good deal of experience in doing machine computations, they knew in a general way what the essential ingredients of such a language would have to be.

One of their biggest surprises was the way the machine went about translating FORTRAN sentences. Often there were machine instructions that did not seem to arise from any given FORTRAN expression, and in some contexts a FORTRAN expression produced no machine-language instructions at all. (Ziller told me that they would put something in and then go around saying, "Look what it did now!") When the system was fairly well advanced, they began racing their FORTRAN programs against machine-language programs produced for the same job by a human programmer.

They would actually run the two programs on the machine, with a stopwatch in hand, to see if the machine-produced program was significantly slower. In the end, they found that for most standard problems the machine-produced FORTRAN program was about as efficient as a good handmade program. (It was obvious from the start, of course, that there would be an immense saving in time in the preparation of the program by machine.) I asked Backus how he and his colleagues had hit upon the specific phrases that are now part of FORTRAN. He told me that members of the group would suggest phrases, and then by trial and error they would see if they worked out on the computer. After FORTRAN was released to the public in 1957, a number of minor flaws and deficiencies came to light, and it was about a year before most of these could be ironed out. As soon as the program became fully operational, in the late nineteen-fifties, Backus said that most of the fun and challenge of developing it were lost for him, and for a while he turned his attention to other things. He is an I.B.M. Fellow—a position that gives him complete freedom to spend his time as he likes, and he is back doing research on programming theory.

The I.B.M. people had invited me to visit their plant, in Poughkeepsie, where many of the large computers are made, and I was very glad to accept the invitation. The plant consists of several enormous buildings on the south side of the town. Here, one can see the entire assembly of a computer, all the way from the manufacture and testing of the individual magnetic cores to the final assembly and testing of the machine. As one might expect, a good deal of the work is automated. This provides more, rather than less, flexibility in the process of constructing a machine. For example, the final panel wiring is done automatically by a Gardner-Denver machine that threads hundreds and hundreds of wires according to a circuit diagram that is itself stored on magnetic tape in a computer. I was especially taken by the sight of a whole floor of assembled computers—each with the name of its sponsor tacked over it—undergoing final tests. It is the only time I have seen the inner works of a modern computer, and they are something to behold—a veritable regimental display of colored wires and gadgets swarming together in orderly patterns. It is a dazzling and awesome sight.

iv

------------▶

IF there is one word that characterizes the history of computers since 1950, the word is probably "proliferation"—proliferation in the number of computers, in the number of people using computers, and in the range of applications of the machines. In 1954, the first computer designed for business-data processing, a UNIVAC, was delivered to General Electric, in Louisville. By September, 1962, there were an estimated 16,187 computers, worth about four and a half billion dollars when new, installed in the United States. And the machines themselves are continuing to improve. Computers perform about one hundred thousand additions a second. Machines can read data from magnetic tapes and store them at a rate of about a hundred thousand characters a second. A high-speed automatic printer can record data from tape at about a thousand lines a minute. Modern computers perform somewhere between one billion and ten billion consecutive operations without error. The next generation of machines, already in the advanced design stage, will probably have basic machine times of a billionth of a second—as compared to a millionth of a second for the present-day machines—which means they will very likely be able to do a billion operations a second. As the machines increase in speed and efficiency, there is an inevitable increase in the sophistication of the programs that they can handle; a very complex program may contain as many as a hundred thousand machine instructions. A survey carried out by a magazine called *Computers and Automation* indicated six hundred areas of application of computers, ranging from medical diagnosis (computers correlate complicated data) to the analysis of literary styles (computers determine the frequency with which certain words and word patterns arise). One of the most remarkable applications is in the field of language translation. The first step in doing such a translation is to give each letter a numerical code. Words can then be stored in the computer memory as sequences of numbers, which means that the computer can tell when two words are the same by comparing the two numbers. A dictionary of, say, Russian-English words and grammatical constructions is stored numerically in the machine, and a text can be translated by comparing its content to the entries in the dictionary. Such applications are a triumph of programming, for the programmer must first formulate apparently qualitative problems so that they become essentially quantitative. As Lady Lovelace said, the Analytical Engine can only perform "whatever we *know how to order it* to perform."

After one has learned something about the extremely rapid development of computers since World War Two, one inevitably wonders whether there are any foreseeable limits to their future development. In this connection, it is interesting to make a few approximate comparisons between computer characteristics and some of the characteristics of the human brain. The basic cell of the human nervous system is known as a neuron. When neurons are suitably stimulated, they absorb or emit nerve impulses, which travel along fibres called axons. A neuron is about the size of a large organic molecule—that is, about a hundred-thousandth of a centimetre in diameter—while the axons sometimes extend for several feet. The disturbance generated by the neuron travels along the axon as an electrical pulse; concurrent with this electrical activity along the axon there also occur chemical changes. The nerve impulses travel along the axons at various speeds, but the highest is thought to be in the neighborhood of ten thousand centimetres a second. This should be compared with the speed of light, which is also the speed at which electrical signals travel in a computer—about thirty billion centimetres a second. (According to Einstein's theory of relativity, the speed of light is also the maximum speed at which any signal can travel.) The human brain, which weighs about a pound, has a volume of about a thousand cubic centimetres and contains about ten billion neurons. This figure might be compared to the number of magnetic cores in a modern computer memory—roughly a million—but in making such a comparison, one must keep in mind the fact that memory is only one of the functions of the brain. Indeed, the brain's ten billion neurons are organized to do a whole variety of mental tasks. To oversimplify, it appears as if they act individually as switching units or relays. When the neuron is stimulated, it "fires"—emits an electro-chemical pulse, after which there is a period of about a hundredth of a second during which the neuron cannot be fired again. In this sense, the neuron acts like a digital unit—like a vacuum tube, for example, which also transmits an electrical pulse when suitably activated. It appears moreover as if neurons can be "conditioned." If one neuron transmits a pulse to a nearby neuron repeatedly, a physiological change takes place in the firing neuron so that it becomes more efficient as a transmitter of pulses to this neighbor.

The nervous system exhibits not only digital aspects (the transmission of electrical pulses), but also analogical aspects (muscular contractions produce changes in blood pressure). Von Neumann, in an essay entitled "The General and Logical Theory of Automata," gave the control of blood pressure by the nervous system as an example of how the two are interconnected:

> . . . the mechanism which keeps the blood pressure constant is of this mixed type. The nerve which senses and reports the blood pressure does it by a sequence of neural impulses, that is, in a digital manner. The muscular contraction which this impulse system induces may still be described as a superposition of many digital impulses. The influence of such a contraction on the blood stream is, however, hydrodynamical, and hence analogy. The reaction of the pressure thus produced back on the nerve which reports the pressure closes the circular feedback, and at this point the analogy procedure again goes over into a digital one. The comparisons between the living organisms and the computing machines are, therefore, certainly imperfect at this point. The living organisms are very complex—part digital and part analogy mechanisms. The computing machines, at least in their recent forms to which I am referring in this discussion, are purely digital.

Von Neumann points out that in reporting a quantity like the blood pressure the nervous system uses a kind of code in which the size of the quantity is made to correspond essentially to the frequency of the pulses transmitted. The information is read by counting pulses, and this insures a high degree of reliability in the system. "If you express a number of the order of a million by counting and miss a count the result is only irrelevantly changed," von Neumann says. "If you express it by [decimal or binary] expansion, a single error in a single digit may vitiate the entire result." In sum, the nervous system behaves in part like a digital computer and in part like an analogue calculator and, hence, there is some imprecision in any comparison of the brain to a digital computer. There are, roughly speaking, about two hundred thousand electronic components in a large computer—besides the million or so magnetic cores in the memory—that perform non-memory functions, such as logic and control. These occupy a volume of about a hundred thousand cubic centimetres. Thus, the brain has about ten thousand times as many components as a large computer, and they occupy about a hundredth of the volume. The basic reaction time for a neuron is estimated to be about a thousandth of a second, as compared to a millionth of a second for an electronic-computer component. Hence, compared to a computer, the brain has a much larger set of components packed into a much tinier volume, but functioning rather slowly. This undoubtedly means that the brain operates by making use of as many of its components as possible at any one time. A system with a few very fast components will operate most efficiently by using them in rapid succession, or serially, whereas a system like the brain, with many comparatively slow components, will make up for the slowness by processing information in parallel chains. As von Neumann put it:

> The natural componentry [the brain] favours automata with more but slower organs. Hence it is to be expected that an efficiently organized large natural automaton (like the human nervous system) will tend to pick up as many logical (or informational) items as possible simultaneously, and process them simultaneously, while an efficiently organized large artificial automaton (like a large modern computing machine) will be more likely to do things successively—one thing at a time, or at any rate not so many things at a time; that is, large and efficient natural automata are likely to be highly *parallel*, while large and efficient artificial automata will tend to be less so, and rather to be *serial*.

It is possible to imagine future machines with as many components as the brain simply as enlargements of the present machines. One might imagine, for example, just taking ten thousand memories of the present size and putting them together. It is clear that such a contraption—if it could be built—would have a volume of many cubic feet. Therefore, the speed of light would begin to play an important role. An electric pulse can travel a foot in a billionth of a second, a thousand feet in a millionth of a second. But the rhythm of the present computers is measured in millionths of a second; the characteristic electronic pulses in the machine, which determine the length of the machine cycles, last something less than a millionth of a second. Hence, given existing components, one could not enlarge a computer memory a great deal without having the time it takes a signal to travel from place to place in the memory become comparable to the basic times of the machine itself—a situation that would result in a great deal of inefficiency.

It has become clear not only that the number of neurons in the brain is very much larger than the number of components in a computer but also that the basic principles of organization must be very different. A computer is constructed according to a precise predetermined plan—a wiring diagram —in which all the connections between the components are spelled out in detail. A completed computer exhibits very little "redundancy"; that is, if part of the memory, for example, is removed, the machine simply will not operate. On the other hand, there is a good deal of evidence to suggest that there is considerable redundancy in the operation of the brain. Some of the brain can be removed without noticeably impairing, say, memory, and it appears, moreover, that, if necessary, different parts of the brain can sometimes take over each other's functions. Indeed, there does not appear to be any special organ in the brain that can, for example, be associated with memory. The most widely accepted picture of the brain is that it is a vast network of neurons which together can perform all the different mental functions. In his book, *The Physical Foundations of Biology,* Dr. W. M. Elsasser summarizes this point of view as follows:

> When the histologist looks at the brain he sees something which is very reminiscent of large electronic computers. He sees a small number of basic components repeated over and over again. All the complexity lies in the innumerable interconnections, not in the variety of basic components. So far as we know, the brain consists exclusively of neurons. Again so far as we know, a neuron does nothing but conduct electrochemical pulses from its head end to its tail end. . . . Thus if one is to study the physiological background of memory one might start with such a model of interconnected neurons. We do not claim that this model is altogether true, but it is simple and presents itself on the basis of anatomical data. There is no anatomical evidence for a storage organ used to file away the immense amount of information which every person retains in his memory.

The fact that there is so much interchangeability among parts of the brain and the associated fact that a damaged brain tends to repair itself by reestablishing new connections among the neurons to take the place of the old ones must mean that the neurons are not connected together according to a rigorous wiring diagram like that of a computer; indeed, it is quite likely that most of the connections among the neurons in the brain develop at random. This is suggested by a consideration of the amount of information that it would take to specify all the connections that exist among the neurons; some, at least, of the ten billion neurons have several thousand connections, so it would be necessary to "blueprint" about ten thousand billion connections. From what is known about the genes that govern the growth pattern of the newborn individual, it seems very unlikely that the genes themselves can carry this much information.

It is perhaps difficult to understand how such a randomly connected system can learn. (An ordinary computer actually cannot be said to learn, since whenever it tackles a problem, however similar the problem may be to previous ones it has done, it must be programmed all over again.) As it happens, a remarkable electronic model demonstrating some of the learning aspects of randomly organized systems has been constructed. It is called the Perceptron, and it was conceived in 1958 by Professor F. Rosenblatt, of Cornell University. The original, or Mark I, version of the Perceptron was constructed at the Cornell Aeronautical Laboratories in 1959, and it and its successors have been the subject of intensive study. The Mark I is built in three levels. The first level consists of a grid of photocells—four hundred of them —which corresponds to the retina of the eye, and to which light stimuli are presented as they would be to an eye. The photocells are connected with a group of components called associator units, on the second level, which collect electrical impulses that have been transmitted from the photocells. The wiring that connects the photocells to the associator units is set up at random; in the Mark I there are five hundred and twelve associator units, and each one can have as many as forty random connections with the photocells. The third level consists of eight response units—components that respond to signals from the associator units. A given associator unit will signal to the response units only if the signal it itself receives is above a certain threshold. (Neurons, too, appear to be activated only if the signals they receive are above a certain threshold.) Hence, when the Perceptron is shown a pattern, a connection is made with the associators; there is no way of predicting in advance what this connection will be, but in any event some of the associator units are activated and, in turn, trigger the response units. The Perceptron learns to recognize shapes. When it is shown an illuminated "A," it responds in a certain manner. Then if it is shown another "A," shaped somewhat differently or in a different part of its visual field, it may or may not respond in the same way. If it responds in the same way, it has recognized the "A." If not, then the signals from those associators that have been activated are modified, and it is shown the "A" once again, and so on. In practice, the Mark I learns to identify letters perfectly after about forty exposures. The Perceptron's process of learning is an evolutionary one. At the first exposure to the changed "A," some aspects of its response will be "right"—appropriate to the recognition of an "A"—and some will be "wrong." If the wrong responses are suppressed, eventually all surviving responses will be correct, and the system will have learned to recognize the "A." If the random system is complex enough so that some of its responses to the new "A" are right, the Perceptron can be made to learn to recognize it by sufficient reinforcement of these responses.

The fact that we are born with instincts that we apparently inherit from our parents—that not everything is learned from scratch—indicates that not all of the organization of the brain can be random. Some of it must be "deterministic"—must be included in the information carried by the genes we receive from our parents. Dr. Rosenblatt and his group have also developed models that combine a partly random and partly deterministic organization. For example, if one restricts oneself to deforming the letters presented to the Perceptron in a particular way, such as expanding them or rotating them, then it is possible to alter the electronics of the Perceptron so as to take advantage of this restriction and thus to enable the Perceptron to learn more efficiently than if it were only randomly wired. In other words, by anticipating the shapes of the objects that the Perceptron will be shown one may alter its design so as to enable it to recognize them better. It seems likely that the brain has some such combination of "deterministic" organization, dictated by what the experience of the race indicates that the newborn child is likely to find in its environment, and a "random" component that enables it to learn in a wide variety of unanticipated situations.

Since the brain, when damaged, has a tendency to repair itself, its organization is clearly such that the defective parts become as inconspicuous as possible. On the other hand, the computer, which must be repaired when it breaks down, is designed so that defects show up as conspicuously as possible—so that they can be tracked down and corrected. Von Neumann noted:

> The basic principle of dealing with malfunctions in nature is to make their effect as unimportant as possible and to apply correctives, if they are necessary at all, at leisure. In our dealings with artificial automata, on the other hand, we require an immediate diagnosis. Therefore, we are trying to arrange the automata in such a manner that errors will become as conspicuous as possible, and intervention and correction follow immediately. In other words, natural organisms are constructed to make errors as inconspicuous, as harmless as possible. Artificial automata are designed to make errors as conspicuous, as disastrous, as possible. The rationale of

this difference is not far to seek. Natural organisms are sufficiently well conceived to be able to operate even when malfunctions have set in. They can operate in spite of malfunctions, and their subsequent tendency is to remove these malfunctions. An artificial automaton could certainly be designed so as to be able to operate normally in spite of a limited number of malfunctions in certain limited areas. Any malfunction, however, represents a considerable risk that some generally degenerating process has already set in within the machine. It is, therefore, necessary to intervene immediately, because a machine which has begun to malfunction has only rarely a tendency to restore itself, and will probably go from bad to worse.

Interestingly, the Perceptron can be partly destroyed—some of its associators can be removed —without damage to its learning operation. The machine utilizes new paths among the remaining associators much as a damaged brain does when it begins to recover its functions. The brain and the Perceptron, unlike the computer, are not specialized for doing arithmetic operations, and the computer does not learn. Perhaps future computers, with numbers of components comparable to those in the brain, will be able to combine functions. If a computer is ever built that does involve nearly as many components as the brain, it would probably be very useful if much of its organization could be random. In this case one would not need to blue-print such a vast array of connections and, more importantly, one might rely on the machine to repair or suppress its malfunctions, relieving the user of the formidable job of searching around among, say, a billion component parts to find a few that may have gone bad.

v
---------▶

APART from the physical limitations of computers, many people have wondered whether there is some intrinsic difference between human thought and the activity of a computer. This is, to some extent, a continuation of the long-standing argument in biology between the "vitalists" and the "mecha-nists." The mechanists claim that the human or-ganism is merely a machine—a very complex one, to be sure—while the vitalists claim that there is an essential vital force possessed by the living hu-man organism and that this cannot be duplicated mechanically. The same controversy arises when people ask, "Do computing machines really think?" So little is understood about the processes of human thought that when the question is formulated in this way, it can hardly be answered. (It is, of course, beside the point that when we think, we think in a language that is the language in which we speak. The connection between that language and the actual functioning of the neurons must be at least as complex and remote as the connection between, say, a FORTRAN instruction and the operation of the machine circuits in carrying out the instruction.)

There is, however, another way of putting the question—a way that was suggested by the late Alan Turing, a brilliant English mathematician—that is answerable, in principle: "Are the responses to questions made by a given computing machine indistinguishable from the responses to the same questions made by a given person?" In other words, is it possible to distinguish between a given computer and a given person simply by communicating with them? Turing proposed a game—now known as the Identification Game, or the Turing Game—that could be played either with three people or with two people and a computer, and that could be used to settle the question of the distinguishability of people from computers. Three people can play the Turing Game as follows: Assume one of the players to be a woman and another a man. (The sex of the third is irrelevant.) The man and the woman remain in one room and communicate with the third player only by means of type-written messages. They disguise their identity in the messages by calling themselves, say, X and Y. The third player can ask the two others any questions he likes by sending in a typewritten questionnaire, his object being to find out whether it is X or Y who is the woman. The woman attempts to reveal her identity by her answers, while the man attempts to disguise his by giving false answers. The questioner must use a rather sophisticated strategy to learn the truth—for example, if he simply asks, "Do you wear a dress?" both X and Y will say "Yes," and he will be no wiser than before. Now, Turing proposed to let the computer play the role of X or Y and let the third player discover "which of the two, X or Y, is human." If the third player can't decide this, the computer has passed its intelligence test.

Turing even proposed, somewhat facetiously, the lines along which the questioning might go:

Q: Please write me a sonnet on the subject of the Forth Bridge.

A: Count me out on this one. I never could write poetry.

Q: Add 34957 to 70764.

A: (Pause about 30 seconds and then give as answer) 105621.

Q: Do you play chess?

A: Yes.

Q: I have K at my K1, and no other pieces.

You have only K at K6 and R at R1. It is your move. What do you play?

A: (After a pause of 15 seconds) R—R8 mate.

Turing continued:

The question and answer method seems to be suitable for introducing almost any one of the fields of human endeavor that we wish to include. We do not wish to penalize the machine for its inability to shine in beauty competitions, nor to penalize a man for losing in a race against an aeroplane. The conditions of our game make these disabilities irrelevant.

As yet there are no computers that can successfully play Turing's game.

Curiously, Turing's most important work, on the general theory of computers, was done before the war, when no digital computer of the type that he was considering had actually been built. Turing's achievement was to give a completely abstract characterization of a digital computer—a characterization that focuses on the logical organization of computers by freeing the discussion of them from any considerations of hardware. Turing's abstract computer, or "Turing machine," as it is known, is organized this way: There is an arbitrarily long tape that runs through the machine. The tape is divided up into squares, and on each square there may be a 1 or a 0. In other words, information is stored on the tape in binary. The machine, whose internal details are completely unspecified, scans the tape one square at a time. Sometimes, after its scanning, the machine will alter what is on the tape and change a o into a 1 or a 1 into a o. The machine consists of a collection of stored instructions. In a single move, the machine scans a square and chooses its next instruction. It may also move the tape forward or backward by one square. Such a machine can perform a variety of "calculations," and Turing was able to prove several remarkable theorems about them. In the first place, he proved that in the mathematical sense there must exist universal "Turing machines." Universal Turing machines are Turing machines that can be programmed to do any computation or logical operation that any other Turing machine can do. In other words, universal Turing machines can be programmed to imitate any other Turing machine. In a book entitled *Computability and Unsolvability*, Dr. Martin Davis, of the Belfer Graduate School of Science of Yeshiva University, who is an authority on Turing machines, notes that "the existence of universal Turing machines confirms the belief of those working with digital computers that it is possible to construct a single 'all-purpose' digital computer on which can be programmed (subject of course to limitations of time and memory capacity) any problem that could be programmed for any conceivable deterministic digital computer."

In the second place, Turing was able to show

that there were questions that Turing machines cannot answer. Of course, any *actual* computing machine can be asked many questions that it cannot answer, simply because no one has devised a program for it that will answer them, or because a computation designed to answer them would be prohibitively long. But this is not Turing's point. His point is that there must exist problems for which programs cannot be devised in principle. An example is the so-called "Halting Problem." This is the problem of deciding whether a given Turing machine with a given tape will ever stop computing or whether it will continue indefinitely. Turing was able to show that there must exist at least one Turing machine for which this question is, in principle, undecidable. One cannot devise a program to determine whether or not the machine will stop computing. Turing's result is a variation on a remarkable theorem that was proved in 1931 by Professor Kurt Gödel, of the Institute for Advanced Study. Gödel's Theorem showed that in a logical system as rich as arithmetic there must be at least one proposition whose truth or falsity is undecidable. There simply exists no proof, and there cannot exist any proof, of the truth or falsity of the undecidable statement in the language of the system within which the statement was formulated. Gödel's result can be translated into the language of Turing machines, and if a Turing machine is asked the undecidable question, it will give either no answer or a false one.

Some people have taken Turing's result as a proof

that machine intelligence, compared to human intelligence, is definitely limited. Turing himself did not think there was very much depth in this view, and in a marvelous essay entitled "Can a Machine Think?" he wrote:

> Whenever one of these machines is asked the appropriate critical question and gives a definite answer, we know that this answer must be wrong, and this gives us a certain feeling of superiority. Is this feeling illusory? It is no doubt quite genuine, but I do not think too much importance should be attached to it. We too often give wrong answers to questions ourselves to be justified in being very pleased at such evidence of fallibility on the part of the machines. Further, our superiority can only be felt on such an occasion in relation to the one machine over which we have scored our petty triumph. There would be no question of triumphing simultaneously over *all* machines. In short then, there might be men cleverer than any given machine, but, then again, there might be other machines cleverer again, and so on.

However one may feel about attributing intelligence to computers, it must be clear that with their rapid development a new force has come into the world. The history of electronic computers is only twenty years old, and they are still sufficiently simple for one to have a sense of understanding in detail how they work, and therefore of being in control. (Someone has remarked, "You can always pull out the plug.") But computers are already being used to design other computers, and it is quite possible that future generations of machines, which have been designed by machines, or which are not organized according to an entirely deterministic plan, may be beyond our complete understanding. Turing, for one, seemed to accept this possibility as a foregone conclusion. Shortly after his tragic death—he died, perhaps by suicide, at the age of forty-two, in 1954—his mother, Sara Turing, wrote a moving and lovely book about his life. In it, she quotes a letter she received from the wife of one of his closest colleagues, the English mathematician M. H. A. Newman. Mrs. Newman wrote, "I remember sitting in our garden at Bowdon about 1949 while Alan and my husband discussed the machine [Turing had played a leading role in the construction of a large digital computer known as MADAM—for Manchester Automatic Digital Machine—at Manchester University] and its future activities. I couldn't take part in the discussion and it was one of many that had passed over my head, but suddenly my ear picked up a remark which sent a shiver down my back. Alan said reflectively, 'I suppose when it gets to that stage we shan't know how it does it.'"

A Selected Bibliography

(I have selected for this bibliography only those books and articles that I felt would be readable for someone without an extensive technical background.)

I

The FORTRAN Language

Clear accounts of the details of the language are given in: *A* FORTRAN *Primer*, Elliot I. Organick. Reading, Mass.: Addison-Wesley, 1963; I.B.M. FORTRAN manual—F28-8074-1 (1961). Programming Systems Publications, I.B.M. Corporation, P.O. Box 390, Poughkeepsie, N.Y.

II

Babbage, and Lady Lovelace
Faster Than Thought—Edited by B. V. Bowden.
London: Sir Isaac Pitman & Sons, 1953. The essays in
Dr. Bowden's collection give a good account of the
field of automatic computation as it was in 1953. His
own essays on Babbage and the history of computation are both informative and delightful.

Charles Babbage and His Calculating Engines. Selected writing by Charles Babbage and Others. Edited
and with an introduction by Philip and Emily Morri-
son. New York: Dover Publications, Inc., 1961. The
Morrisons' collection of Babbagenia is a splendid
source of material by and about the great man. Large
portions of *Passages from the Life of a Philosopher*
are reproduced, and the Morrisons have written a fascinating historical introduction to his work.

Both of these books contain a great deal of material
about Lady Lovelace.

III

Computing Machines
Essentially, all texts on modern computers require
a considerable background in electronics to make
much out of them. The ones listed were among the
most readable for me.

Automatic Digital Computers, M. V. Wilkes. New
York: Wiley, 1956. Although much of this book is
quite technical, Mr. Wilkes also deals with the history
of the machines and the comparison between the modern computers and the Analytical Engine.

Giant Brains, Edmund C. Berkeley. New York: Science Editions, 1961. Mr. Berkeley's book is mostly con-
cerned with the generation of computers that were
built before 1950. His book gives a detailed account of

the early relay computers as well as the Bush analogue calculator.

There is a comprehensive popular article on computers, written by Dr. H. H. Goldstine, for the *Encyclopædia Britannica*.

"Preliminary Discussion of the Logical Design of an Electronic Computing Instrument," by A. W. Burks, H. H. Goldstine and J. von Neumann. This classic paper in the field of electronic computing was reprinted in an abbreviated form in the September and October 1962 issues of *Datamation* magazine. The reprint, annotated by Paul Armer of the Rand Corporation, is especially useful since Mr. Armer has retained those parts of the original paper that contain ideas still widely used. Much of the discussion can be followed by an interested lay reader.

"The Evolution of Computing Machines and Systems," by R. Serrell, M. M. Astrahan, G. W. Patterson and I. B. Pyne. Proceedings of the IRE, May, 1962. This paper gives a brief account of the evolution of computers to the present. Most of the major machines are discussed and their characteristics are compared. There is also a useful bibliography for further reading and the authors have included a number of photographs of different computers and computer designers.

Mathematics and Computers, George R. Stibitz and Jules A. Larrivee. New York: McGraw-Hill, 1957. This book deals, in a semipopular way, with a number of aspects of computers and numerical analysis. The emphasis is on the logical and mathematical facets of the subject. Mr. Stibitz is one of the pioneers in the field of relay computers and some of the book describes his early work.

John von Neumann (1903-1957)

There is as yet no real biography of this extraordinary man. Shortly after his death, the *Bulletin of the American Mathematical Society* devoted an entire issue (Vol. 64, No. 3, Part 2, May 1958) to his life and career. In the issue, there is a long biographical sketch written by Dr. Stanislaw Ulam, who was for many years a close friend and colleague of von Neumann's. There is also an excellent summary by Dr. Claude Shannon of von Neumann's contribution to the theory of Automata.

IV

The Computer and the Brain

A vast amount has been written on this fascinating subject. The following references were most useful to me.

The Computer and the Brain, John von Neumann. New Haven, Conn.: Yale University Press, 1958. Part of this book is in finished form and part consists of fragments that were written at the end of von Neumann's life. All of the book repays careful reading.

Information Storage and Neural Control. Compiled and edited by William S. Fields and Walter Abbot. Springfield, Ill.: Charles C. Thomas, 1963. This book presents a collection of essays on information processing in nervous systems. The level is technical.

"The Perceptron: A Model for Brain Functioning I," by H. D. Block. *Reviews of Modern Physics,* Vol. 34, No. 1 (Jan. 1962). Dr. Block presents a detailed discussion of the Perceptron. The earlier parts of this paper can be followed by an interested layman. Dr. Rosenblatt and his group have published a number of technical papers on the Perceptron and related studies.

"The General and Logical Theory of Automata," by John von Neumann. This fascinating and profound essay is reprinted in Volume 4 of *The World of Mathematics,* edited by James Newman. New York: Simon and Schuster, 1956. Von Neumann's essay covers all of the aspects of the relation between the computer and the brain that are treated in this book.

V

Turing and Turing Machines

In the same volume of *The World of Mathematics* in which von Neumann's article appears, there is a brilliant article by Turing entitled, "Can a Machine Think?" His article has been the basis of a great deal of the thinking on this question. Turing discusses Turing machines, as does von Neumann in the article cited above. The subject is an intrinsically difficult one, and there is not a great deal of popular literature available on it.

Index

--------- ▶

About the Author

Jeremy Bernstein is the first physicist on the staff of *The New Yorker,* and, in addition to *The Analytical Engine,* his work for that magazine includes book reviews, "Talk of the Town" pieces, and a profile of T. D. Lee and C. N. Yang, two Chinese physicists. He is also the author of more than thirty papers which have appeared in the scientific journals and has, since 1962, been associate professor of physics at New York University. Mr. Bernstein was born in Rochester, New York on December 31, 1929, attended Columbia Grammar School in New York City and studied for eight years at Harvard University, from which he received his A.B., a Masters in Mathematics and a Doctorate in Physics. He then worked for two years as a Research Associate at the Harvard Cyclotron Laboratory, and two subsequent years at the Institute for Advanced Study at Princeton. He has also been a physicist at Los Alamos and at Brookhaven National Laboratories and he traveled to Europe on a National Science Foundation Post-Doctoral Fellowship in Paris, Vienna and Geneva. Mr. Bernstein is now a frequent visiting physicist at CERN (Centre Européen pour la Recherche Nucléaire) in Geneva, and serves as a consultant both to the General Atomics Corporation and the RAND Corporation.